S0-CAA-041

SPIRIT
of TRUTH

"But when He comes, the Spirit of Truth,
He will guide you to all truth."

JOHN 16:13

STUDENT WORKBOOK
Living as a Disciple of Christ

SOPHIA INSTITUTE
FOR TEACHERS

About Sophia Institute for Teachers

Sophia Institute for Teachers was launched in 2013 by Sophia Institute to renew and rebuild Catholic culture through service to Catholic education. With the goal of nurturing the spiritual, moral, and cultural life of souls, and an abiding respect for the role and work of teachers, we strive to provide materials and programs that are at once enlightening to the mind and ennobling to the heart; faithful and complete, as well as useful and practical. Sophia Institute is a 501(c)(3) nonprofit organization founded in 1983.

Excerpts from the English translation of Rite of Baptism for Children © 1969, International Commission on English in the Liturgy Corporation (ICEL); excerpts from the English translation of Rite of Christian Initiation of Adults © 1985, ICEL; excerpts from the English translation of The Roman Missal © 2010, ICEL; excerpts from the English translation of The Order of Celebrating Matrimony © 2013, ICEL; excerpts from the English translation of The Order of Confirmation © 2013, ICEL. All rights reserved.

Excerpts from the English translation of the *Catechism of the Catholic Church*, Second Edition, © 1994, 1997, 2000 by Libreria Editrice Vaticana–United States Catholic Conference, Washington, D.C. All rights reserved.

Scripture texts in this work are taken from the New American Bible, revised edition © 2010, 1991, 1986, 1970 Confraternity of Christian Doctrine, Washington, D.C., and are used by permission of the copyright owner. All rights reserved. No part of the New American Bible may be reproduced in any form without permission in writing from the copyright owner.

Scriptural Rosary for Justice and Peace © 2017, United States Conference of Catholic Bishops, Washington, DC. Used with permission. All rights reserved. No part of this text may be reprinted without permission in writing from the copyright owner.

Prayer in Defense of Marriage © 2017, United States Conference of Catholic Bishops, Washington, DC. Used with permission. All rights reserved. No part of this text may be reprinted without permission in writing from the copyright owner.

Unless otherwise noted, images in this book are in the public domain.

The Subcommittee on the Catechism, United States Conference of Catholic Bishops, has found this text, copyright 2017, to be in conformity with the *Catechism of the Catholic Church*.

© 2017 by Sophia Institute for Teachers. All rights reserved. Portions of this publication may be photocopied and/or reproduced within the schools which purchased it for educational use only. Written permission must be secured from the publisher to use or reproduce any part of this book outside the school which purchased it in any medium.

Printed in the United States of America, Design by Perceptions Design Studio
Cover image: St. Peter Invited to Walk on the Water, 1766 (oil on canvas), Boucher, Francois (1703-70) /
Cathedrale Saint-Louis, Versailles, France / Bridgeman Images.

Spirit of Truth: Living as a Disciple of Christ Student Workbook
ISBN: 978-1-622824-403
Fifth Printing

Inside this Book

UNIT 1

Personal Growth

In this unit, you will learn about…

› Being made in God's image and likeness.

› The purpose of human existence.

› Physical and sexual growth.

› Emotional and intellectual growth.

› Social growth.

› Spiritual growth.

› Growth in the virtues and in the Gifts of the Holy Spirit.

› Challenges we face in growing and maturing.

Introduction

Human beings are made in God's image and likeness as male and female. This means that every human being possesses dignity because he or she is made in God's image. Every person is called to cooperate with the grace of God and pursue holiness. We live our lives becoming the person God calls us to be. Adolescence in particular is a time of rapid growth, physically, sexually, emotionally, intellectually, socially, and spiritually. Faced with many challenges as we navigate this period of life, we are called to remain close to God, to rely on the example of the saints and the assistance of others, and to grow and mature into the person God calls us to be.

What questions do you have right now about the topics you will be learning about in this unit?

_____

_____

_____

_____

Actual Grace: Help from God in each moment of our lives to choose the good.

Adoration: A form of prayer in which we worship God and express our love for Him.

Beatitude: Happiness or fulfillment. In the Sermon on the Mount Jesus gave the Beatitudes as the perfection of the Ten Commandments. They teach us how to be truly happy, or reach human perfection and fulfillment, which we ultimately find in Heaven.

Chastity: A moral virtue that helps us manage or control our desires for bodily and spiritual pleasure in the way that God intended. Chastity specifically involves self-mastery of sexual feelings. It is also a virtue that helps us choose what is best for others. Jesus Christ is a model of a chaste life.

Communion: Sharing of life with one another. As one human family, we are called to imitate God who as Trinity is a communion of Persons, Father, Son, and Holy Spirit, by loving and serving God and by loving and serving one another.

Complementarity: The condition of completing something else, or making it whole. Made in the image and likeness of God as male and female, men and women together complete or make whole the human race as a reflection of God.

Concupiscence: A tendency, or inclination, to sin that is an effect of Original Sin. Even though Baptism erases the stain of Original Sin, the tendency to sin remains.

Conscience: The gift God gave human beings to be able to use reason in order to judge right from wrong. Conscience is God's voice in our hearts. We have a responsibility to educate ourselves and inform our conscience with prayer and God's word, about what is truly good. A poorly-formed conscience will lead us to sin.

Contrition: A form of prayer in which we have true sorrow for our sins and ask for God's mercy and forgiveness.

Counsel: A Gift of the Holy Spirit that helps us to be more open to what our conscience is saying. It helps us to know right from wrong and to judge whether things will lead us toward God or away from Him.

Dignity: Worthy of honor or respect. All human beings from unborn babies to the elderly have equal dignity as children of God.

Emotions: Feelings. Responses of the body and soul to some experience of the senses. They are neither morally good nor morally bad. They only take on a moral quality when we use our intellect and will to direct them for some morally good or morally bad purpose.

Faith: The Theological Virtue by which we believe in God and all that He has revealed to us, as well as all that His Church teaches us to believe.

Fear of the Lord: A Gift of the Holy Spirit that inspires us to see God as He is, not who we think He might be, and to be in awe of His glory and might.

Fortitude: A Cardinal Virtue that helps us continue when faced with difficulty.

Free Will: One of the faculties of the human soul. It is a person's ability to choose and act based upon knowledge and understanding. Human beings have free will.

Holiness: The fullness of the Christian life and the perfection of charity. To be holy is to be set apart by God. We do not make ourselves holy; rather, holiness comes from God's initiative. We are holy because God is holy and he calls us to Himself.

Hope: The Theological Virtue by which we desire the Kingdom of God and eternal life, and place our trust in all of God's promises to us.

Intercession: A form of prayer in which we ask for God's help for others.

Justice: A Cardinal Virtue that helps us give God and neighbor their due.

Knowledge: A Gift of the Holy Spirit that helps us to know God's plan for our lives and to act upon it. It helps us overcome our weaknesses, sins, and failures.

Love: The Theological Virtue by which we love God above all things and our neighbor as ourselves for the love of God. Also called charity.

Meditative Prayer: A form of prayer in which we engage our minds and hearts in reflection on God and the things of God, often using spiritual readings from Scripture.

Piety: A Gift of the Holy Spirit that helps us show reverence for holy things and for God. It helps us to have the right attitude toward God and to worship Him because we love Him.

Prayer: Raising one's mind and heart to God in praise of His glory, asking for some desired good, giving Him thanks, or asking for His blessing on others. Through a life of prayer we experience a relationship with God.

Prudence: A Cardinal Virtue that helps us to have right reason and put it into action. It helps us to make the right decision at the right time and to find the best way to achieve a good outcome.

Reason (Intellect): One of the faculties of the human soul. It is a person's ability to know and understand. Human beings have an intellect.

Sanctifying Grace: The free gift of God's love and life within our souls given to us by the Holy Spirit. Sanctifying grace heals us of sin and makes us holy. We receive sanctifying grace through the Sacraments, especially in Baptism and Holy Eucharist.

Self-Gift: The ability of a person to give of his time and energy to other people out of love. All human beings are capable of self-gift.

Self-Knowledge: The ability of a person to know himself and to reflect upon his memories, personality, and behavior. All human beings are capable of self-knowledge.

Self-Possession: The ability of a person to have control over what she does and to choose her actions. All human beings are capable of self-possession.

Temperance: A Cardinal Virtue that helps us avoid extremes and find the right balance between too much and too little of the good things in life.

Thanksgiving: A form of prayer in which we show gratitude to God for every gift He has given to us.

Understanding: A Gift of the Holy Spirit that helps us know and understand the truths of our Faith that are beyond our ability to know by ourselves. God's grace helps us to get to the heart of the truth and to know and follow God's will for us.

Virtue: A habit of doing what is good. We build virtues through our own efforts and with God's grace.

Wisdom: A Gift of the Holy Spirit that helps us respect and love God. It perfects our faith, because it helps us to see God for who He is.

Annunciation

BY LEONARDO DA VINCI (C. 1472–1475)

Uffizi Gallery, Florence, Italy.

Annunciation

Annunciation, by Leonardo da Vinci (c. 1472–1475)

Directions: Take some time to quietly view and reflect on the art. Let yourself be inspired in any way that happens naturally. Then think about the questions below, and discuss them with your classmates.

Discussion Questions

1. What event is happening in this scene?

2. Read *Catechism of the Catholic Church* no. 1704 below. What does this passage tell us about ourselves?

    The human person participates in the light and power of the divine Spirit. By his reason, he is capable of understanding the order of things established by the Creator. By free will, he is capable of directing himself toward his true good. He finds his perfection "in seeking and loving what is true and good."

3. Read Luke 1:26-38. How does this painting illustrate this Scripture passage?

4. How does Luke 1:26-38 show that Mary used her reason and free will to agree to God's will for her?

5. How does this painting illustrate that Mary understood and freely chose God's will for her?

6. In Luke 1:30, Gabriel said to Mary, "you have found favor with God." What does this statement imply about Mary's life?

7. How do you think Mary's choice to be the mother of Jesus affected her relationship with God?

8. What are some ways that Mary's life shows us the importance and value of living in God's favor?

Thinking about the Saints

Directions: Choose a young saint to research. After completing your research, answer the questions below.

1. Paragraph 1833 of the *Catechism* tells us that "virtue is a habitual and firm disposition to do good." How would you put this into your own words?

    _____

    _____

    _____

2. What choices did your saint make? How did he or she choose what was truly good?

    _____

    _____

    _____

3. What particular virtues did your saint demonstrate? How?

    _____

    _____

    _____

    _____

Luke 1:38

Mary said, "Behold, I am the handmaid of the Lord. May it be done to me according to your word." Then the angel departed from her.

Genesis 1:27

God created mankind in his image; in the image of God he created them; male and female he created them.

Ephesians 2:10

For we are his handiwork, created in Christ Jesus for the good works that God has prepared in advance, that we should live in them.

_____

_____

_____

_____

_____

_____

_____

_____

1 Corinthians 6:19-20

Do you not know that your body is a temple of the holy Spirit within you, whom you have from God, and that you are not your own? For you have been purchased at a price. Therefore, glorify God in your body.

_____

_____

_____

_____

_____

_____

_____

_____

_____

_____

_____

1 Thessalonians 5:23

May the God of peace himself make you perfectly holy and may you entirely, spirit, soul, and body, be preserved blameless for the coming of our Lord Jesus Christ.

_____

_____

_____

_____

_____

_____

_____

_____

_____

1 John 3:16

The way we came to know love was that he laid down his life for us; so we ought to lay down our lives for our brothers.

Isaiah 11:2

The spirit of the LORD shall rest upon him:
a spirit of wisdom and of understanding,
a spirit of counsel and of strength, a spirit
of knowledge and of fear of the LORD.

---

1 Samuel 16:7

But the LORD said to Samuel: "Do not judge from his appearance or from his lofty stature, because I have rejected him. God does not see as a mortal, who sees the appearance. The LORD looks into the heart."

The Dignity of the Human Person

Directions: Read the following and respond to the questions that follow.

We read in Genesis 1:27 that "God created mankind in his image; in the image of God he created them; male and female he created them." The human person has a unique place in creation. We were specifically created by God in His image and likeness. This is a gift no other creature possesses. The *Catechism of the Catholic Church* no. 357 explains this idea more:

> Being in the image of God the human individual possesses the dignity of a person, who is not just something, but someone.

What does it mean to have dignity? Dignity is the unique worth and value that we possess simply for being human, for being created like God. In being created like God, we are capable of certain things that God is capable of. First of all, we can know ourselves. We can reflect on our memories, our personality, and our behavior. Secondly, we have the gift of free will, meaning we can choose our actions. Sometimes it might feel as if we are acting on instinct, such as when we are surprised or when we are intensely focused on something. But ultimately, we have control over what we do. Finally, we are able to give of our time and our energies to other people out of love. We call these three things *self-knowledge, self-possession,* and *self-gift.*

This dignity is something we all have, no matter what. We are valuable simply because we exist. God created us out of love, and He sustains us by His love. That alone gives us our dignity. Our dignity does not depend on how popular we are or what we look like. It does not depend on how much money we have or what country we were born in. A human life has dignity from the moment of conception. Our dignity does not depend on how old we are, or how sick or close to death we might be.

Our dignity does not depend on any of those things. It does not even increase because of the good we do or decrease because of the mistakes we make. We have dignity simply because we are created in the image and likeness of God. Every single person is valuable because he or she is loved by God.

1. How are human beings created in relation to God?

    _____

2. What do you think it means to be someone rather than something?

    _____

    _____

3. What is self-knowledge? _____

_____

4. What is self-possession? _____

_____

5. What is self-gift? _____

_____

6. Where does our dignity come from? _____

_____

7. Where doesn't our dignity come from? _____

_____

Made for Communion

Directions: Read the information below, then create a list as directed.

Genesis 2 describes the creation of man and woman in detail. Interestingly, after God created Adam, He says, "It is not good for the man to be alone" (Genesis 2:18a). God did not mean we should *never* be alone, of course. Sometimes being alone is helpful so we can rest and gather our thoughts. In the next line it is made clearer what God meant: "I will make a helper suited to him" (Genesis 2:18b). God knew that Adam could not live by himself on the earth forever. It would be too lonely.

The same truth applies to us today.

1. Think about your week. In the space below, write five things you could not have done this week if it were not for other people.

_____

_____

_____

It's not enough simply to be around people. The *Catechism of the Catholic Church* no. 1878 describes the need for unity like this: "There is a certain resemblance between the unity of the divine persons and the fraternity that men are to establish among themselves in truth and love."

You may have heard the word *fraternity* to describe men's groups in college. That's not what the *Catechism* is talking about here. The word *fraternity* comes from the Latin word *frater*, which means "brother." If we want to imitate God as a communion of persons, we need to have a communion with the people around us, like a family. Another word for this is *solidarity*. This is the principle of unity among the human race. We recognize that we are united in one human family, and we commit ourselves to working toward the good of others. The *Catechism of the Catholic Church* no. 1878 goes on to say this: "Love of neighbor is inseparable from love for God."

St. John the Evangelist wrote a letter to an early Church community and said something similar: "If anyone says, 'I love God,' but hates his brother, he is a liar; for whoever does not love a brother whom he has seen cannot love God whom he has not seen. This is the commandment we have from him: whoever loves God must also love his brother" (1 John 4:20-21). These words aren't meant to scare us. Rather, John is making a different point entirely.

2. What point do you think John is emphasizing?

_____

_____

The Map to Happiness

Directions: Read the essay below, then answer the questions that follow.

Every human person is made for happiness. People travel many different roads to try to get there, such as the road of friendship, the road of education, the road of money and power, or the road of easy fun from watching movies or playing video games. These roads have mixed results. They don't always lead to happiness. Our friends might gossip about us, or school might turn out to be more difficult than we thought it would be. Maybe we initially feel good about the money we have, but then we spend it and need more to feel better. Video games can be fun to play, but sometimes it can feel almost painful to turn off the console and get on with our normal life. We need to eat and sleep, and somebody needs to work to pay the electric bill!

It's easy to get lost on the way to happiness. Sometimes we might not even know what we're really looking for. Does happiness exist in doing whatever we want or whatever makes us feel good at the moment? Not necessarily. Have you ever made a decision that you regretted afterward? You freely made a choice, but that choice didn't make you happy. That tells us that it isn't the choice itself that leads to happiness.

Sometimes we think that happiness lies in the body. After we eat a good meal, for example, we can feel very happy and fulfilled. Eventually though, if we ate that same meal over and over again, we'd get tired of it, and it would no longer make us as happy. Happiness is more than just feeling good and having our physical needs met. In fact, we could have all the food and money and entertainment we ever wanted, but if someone we loved suddenly died, we would feel unhappy.

It's very easy for us to get lost on the journey to happiness. Maybe that's because we're not looking for happiness in the right way. If we misspell a street name in our GPS app, we're not going to arrive at the right destination. Similarly, we can think we're moving toward happiness when we're really being led in the wrong direction. However, if we know the right destination, we'll have an easier time finding the right roads to get there. What would a map to happiness look like? What if our destination was actually the very purpose of our creation?

The *Catechism of the Catholic Church* no. 27 tells us: "The desire for God is written in the human heart, because man is created by God and for God; and God never ceases to draw man to himself. Only in God will he find the truth and happiness he never stops searching for."

God has made us for the happiness of His love. The word for this state of blessed happiness is beatitude. The map to beatitude ends with Heaven. Our lives on earth include struggle and difficulty and sin, but God gives us hints of the perfect love of Heaven every day. Think of all the "roads" we've listed so far. It's not that these things don't contribute to happiness. Our friends, our education, our material possessions, the food we eat, the money we make – all of them can make us happy temporarily. The problem comes when we make these things our final *destination*, instead of just one step on the road. We were created for a happiness greater than what these things can provide. The good things in our lives are a taste of Heaven, a small amount of the perfect joy we were created for.

1. What are some of the different roads people follow to find happiness? Why don't they always lead to happiness?

   _____

   _____

   _____

2. Why is happiness more than just doing what we want?

   _____

3. Why is happiness more than meeting our physical needs?

   _____

4. Where do we find ultimate happiness? Why?

   _____

   _____

5. What does the word *beatitude* mean?

   _____

6. How should the different "roads" fit into our life?

   _____

   _____

Reflection Question

We could say that everything truly good in this life offers us a small taste of Heaven. When we think about the good things in our life, it can give us some sense of what awaits us there. What are some of these things in your life? Pick two things in your life that bring you real happiness, and, on your own paper, describe why they remind you of Heaven.

Saint Reflection Questions

Directions: Read the saint cards given to you and complete the chart.

	Saint: _____	Saint: _____
By what do you think this saint would have "defined" him or herself? Why do you think so?		
What example did this saint give for your own call to holiness?		

Reflection Question

Directions: Respond to the following prompt in a well-written paragraph of at least five to seven sentences.

Choose one of the saints you studied and consider his or her greatness. How is the greatness of the saint you chose different from what our world today considers to be greatness? Are you more or less similar to these saints in your own pursuit of holiness? Why or why not?

_____

_____

_____

_____

_____

_____

_____

_____

_____

_____

_____

_____

_____

_____

_____

A Unity of Two

Directions: From the very beginning, human beings were created male and female. We read about this in Genesis 1 and 2. The *Catechism of the Catholic Church* talks about this in more detail. Let's discover more about what it means that man and woman form a unity of two. Read the passages from the *Catechism of the Catholic Church* and then answer the questions that follow each one.

CCC 371

God created man and woman *together* and willed each *for* the other. The Word of God gives us to understand this through various features of the sacred text. "It is not good that the man should be alone. I will make him a helper fit for him." None of the animals can be man's partner. The woman God "fashions" from the man's rib and brings to him elicits on the man's part a cry of wonder, an exclamation of love and communion: "This at last is bone of my bones and flesh of my flesh." Man discovers woman as another "I," sharing the same humanity.

1. *Willed* means "chose." Now that you know this, rewrite the first sentence of CCC 371 in your own words to explain what it might mean.

   _____

   _____

2. Since we are made in the image of God, we know that God makes us as someone, not something. Why couldn't the animals be a suitable partner for a human being?

   _____

   _____

CCC 372

Man and woman were made "for each other" – not that God left them half-made and incomplete: he created them to be a communion of persons, in which each can be "helpmate" to the other, for they are equal as persons ("bone of my bones...") and complementary as masculine and feminine. In marriage God unites them in such a way that, by forming "one flesh," they can transmit human life: "Be fruitful and multiply, and fill the earth." By transmitting human life to their descendants, man and woman as spouses and parents cooperate in a unique way in the Creator's work.

3. What does it mean to say that men and women are "made for each other"?

_____

_____

4. What does it mean that two things are "complementary" to each other?

_____

_____

5. What unique thing are man and woman able to do together, something that no other partnership can?

_____

_____

CCC 2333

Everyone, man and woman, should acknowledge and accept his sexual *identity*. Physical, moral, and spiritual *difference* and *complementarity* are oriented toward the goods of marriage and the flourishing of family life. The harmony of the couple and of society depends in part on the way in which the complementarity, needs, and mutual support between the sexes are lived out.

6. In general, how are men and women different?

_____

_____

_____

_____

7. How do the differences between men and women benefit others?

_____

_____

_____

_____

_____

Litany of St. Joseph

Directions: Read through and pray the litany to yourself. Then underline the three titles of St. Joseph that best describe who you want to be. Then, on the next page, write out the titles you chose and explain why you like these traits and how you want to live them out in your life.

St. Joseph, *pray for us.*

Renowned offspring of David, *pray for us.*

Light of Patriarchs, *pray for us.*

Spouse of the Mother of God, *pray for us.*

Chaste guardian of the Virgin, *pray for us.*

Foster father of the Son of God, *pray for us.*

Diligent protector of Christ, *pray for us.*

Head of the Holy Family, *pray for us.*

Joseph most just, *pray for us.*

Joseph most chaste, *pray for us.*

Joseph most prudent, *pray for us.*

Joseph most strong, *pray for us.*

Joseph most obedient, *pray for us.*

Joseph most faithful, *pray for us.*

Mirror of patience, *pray for us.*

Lover of poverty, *pray for us.*

Model of artisans, *pray for us.*

Glory of home life, *pray for us.*

Guardian of virgins, *pray for us.*

Pillar of families, *pray for us.*

Solace of the wretched, *pray for us.*

Hope of the sick, *pray for us.*

Patron of the dying, *pray for us.*

Terror of demons, *pray for us.*

Protector of Holy Church, *pray for us.*

God made him the lord of his household, *and prince over all his possessions.*

Let us pray. O God, in Your ineffable providence You were pleased to choose Blessed Joseph to be the spouse of Your most holy Mother; grant, we beg You, that we may be worthy to have him for our intercessor in heaven whom on earth we venerate as our protector: You who live and reign forever and ever. Amen.

Image above: *Saint Joseph and the Christ Child*, The Museum of Fine Arts, Houston.

Title 1: _____

_____

_____

_____

_____

_____

Title 2: _____

_____

_____

_____

_____

_____

Title 3: _____

_____

_____

_____

_____

_____

Litany of Loreto

Directions: Read through and pray the litany to yourself. Then underline the three titles of Mary that best describe who you want to be. In the space below, write out the titles you chose and explain why you like these traits and how you want to live them out in your own life.

Holy Mary, *pray for us.*

Holy Mother of God, *pray for us.*

Holy Virgin of Virgins, *pray for us.*

Mother of Christ, *pray for us.*

Mother of divine grace, *pray for us.*

Mother most pure, *pray for us.*

Mother most chaste, *pray for us.*

Mother inviolate, *pray for us.*

Mother undefiled, *pray for us.*

Mother most amiable, *pray for us.*

Mother most admirable, *pray for us.*

Mother of good counsel, *pray for us.*

Mother of our Creator, *pray for us.*

Mother of our Savior, *pray for us.*

Mother of the Church, *pray for us.*

Virgin most prudent, *pray for us.*

Virgin most venerable, *pray for us.*

Virgin most renowned, *pray for us.*

Virgin most powerful, *pray for us.*

Virgin most merciful, *pray for us.*

Virgin most faithful, *pray for us.*

Mirror of justice, *pray for us.*

Seat of wisdom, *pray for us.*

Cause of our joy, *pray for us.*

Spiritual vessel, *pray for us.*

Vessel of honor, *pray for us.*

Singular vessel of devotion, *pray for us.*

Mystical rose, *pray for us.*

Tower of David, *pray for us.*

Tower of ivory, *pray for us.*

House of gold, *pray for us.*

Ark of the covenant, *pray for us.*

Gate of heaven, *pray for us.*

Morning star, *pray for us.*

Health of the sick, *pray for us.*

Refuge of sinners, *pray for us.*

Comforter of the afflicted, *pray for us.*

Help of Christians, *pray for us.*

Queen of Angels, *pray for us.*

Queen of Patriarchs, *pray for us.*

Image above: *Nuestra Señora De Loreto*, Bluedreamer2011 / Flickr.com.

Queen of Prophets, *pray for us.*

Queen of Apostles, *pray for us.*

Queen of Martyrs, *pray for us.*

Queen of Confessors, *pray for us.*

Queen of Virgins, *pray for us.*

Queen of all Saints, *pray for us.*

Queen conceived without original sin,
pray for us.

Queen assumed into heaven, *pray for us.*

Queen of the most holy Rosary, *pray for us.*

Queen of families, *pray for us.*

Queen of peace, *pray for us.*

Pray for us, O holy Mother of God, *that we may be made worthy of the promises of Christ.*

Let us pray. Grant, we beseech Thee, O Lord God, that we Thy servants may enjoy perpetual health of mind and body, and by the glorious intercession of blessed Mary, ever Virgin, may we be freed from present sorrow, and rejoice in eternal happiness. Through Christ our Lord. Amen.

Title 1: _____

_____

_____

_____

_____

Title 2: _____

_____

_____

_____

_____

Title 3: _____

_____

_____

_____

_____

Love vs. Use

Directions: Read the paragraphs below about the difference between love and using. Then, follow the instructions for each reflection question.

The love we have for pizza has a name. It's called *use*. When we use something, we apply our own purposes to that thing. In other words, we love pizza because we use it for some purpose: to make us happy, because it's delicious, and so forth. Though it is wrong to do so, sometimes we use people too. When we use a person, we don't really see him or her as a person with unique thoughts, feelings, and desires. Instead we see some*thing* we can "use" for our own purpose. When we use another person, we want to get something out of him or her for ourselves, some good feeling or benefit from that person. Using *things* is okay, as long as those things are used properly and according to the moral law. Using *people* is never okay. People are not things to be used.

Reflection Question

1. Read the situation below and determine why it is an example of *using* another. Explain your answer on the lines below.

   Nate doesn't have a lot of friends in his class. When he gets the newest video-game system for Christmas, his mom says he can invite some people over to play. Nate asks Brandon and Jamie if they want to come over, but they say no. Next Nate asks Peter. This time he makes sure to say that he has a new video-game system. Peter says yes, he will come over. Brandon and Jamie overhear the conversation and find out that Nate has a new video-game system. Later they come up to Nate and say that they want to come over too.

   _____

   _____

   _____

   _____

   _____

   _____

As Catholics, we are called to something different. When Jesus talks about loving other people, He doesn't mean loving them as if they were pizza. He doesn't mean that we love people only if they make us feel good or we benefit from them. The definition of *love* for Catholics is "to will the good of the other." To "will" is to choose. When we truly love someone, we choose what is best for *that person*. When we use another person, we choose what is best for ourselves. With love, we are looking out for other people. Sometimes this means we won't get something out of it right away. It also means that everyone will be taken care of because we're helping each other.

Reflection Question

2. Read the situation below and determine why it is an example of *love*. Explain your answer on the lines below.

   Taylor, Shannon, and Elise are sitting at the lunch table, joking around. Shannon makes a mean comment about Taylor. Taylor immediately looks sad and hurt. Elise is scared, because Shannon is one of the most popular girls in their class. If she stands up for Taylor, Shannon might be mean to her too. Elise takes a deep breath and says, "Shannon, that's not nice, and it's not even true. Don't talk to Taylor like that. It's not right."

   _____

   _____

   _____

   _____

   _____

   _____

   _____

When we think about our interactions as boys and girls, understanding the difference between loving and using are even more important. As we grow up and our bodies change, we are sometimes drawn to other people in a romantic way. When we have romantic feelings for another person, it can be difficult sometimes to tell the difference between loving and using. Therefore, all of our interactions with others – our friendships, and our romantic relationships – should be marked by *chastity*. Chastity is a special virtue that helps us to choose what is best for others, even if our bodies or our emotions want to be selfish.

Chastity is a moral virtue that helps us manage or control our desires for bodily and spiritual pleasure in the way that God intended. Chastity specifically involves self-mastery of sexual feelings. Every baptized person is called to live a chaste life, whether they are married or single. Our best model of chastity (and of all the virtues!) is Jesus Christ.

Reflection Question

3. Read the situation below and determine why it is an example of *using* another. Then describe how the people in the situation could show *love* through *chastity*. Explain your answer on the lines below.

   Juan has friends over for a birthday party. They decide to play "Truth or Dare." When Juan chooses "dare," his friends dare him to kiss Megan. Juan thinks Megan is pretty, and he knows that kissing her will make him look good in front of his friends. Megan knows one of the other girls likes Juan. Megan thinks the other girl is annoying. She knows that kissing Juan will make the other girl mad, so she lets Juan kiss her.

   _____

   _____

   _____

   _____

   _____

   _____

   _____

   _____

Reason-Choose-Feel

Directions: For each of the following scenarios, identify what the person *reasoned* with his or her intellect, *chose* with his or her will, and what *feelings* or *emotions* were involved. For the third situation, identify the reasoning, choices, and feelings of both people.

Situation 1

Liv has always had a place in her heart for animals. She has had pets since she was young and cares about animals and their well-being. Liv is interested in volunteering at an animal shelter. She decides to do some research and finds a shelter near her house. She talks to her mom about good times to volunteer, and her mom helps her sign up to volunteer.

Intellect–Reason:

_____

_____

Will–Choose:

_____

_____

Emotions–Feel:

_____

_____

Situation 2

Every day after school, Tommy has to do his homework. School is difficult for Tommy, so thinking through the assignments isn't easy. After finishing his homework, Tommy is tired and a little discouraged. He often watches TV for hours to forget about his work and feel better.

Intellect—Reason:

_____

_____

Will—Choose:

_____

_____

Emotions—Feel:

_____

_____

Situation 3

Nina doesn't have a lot of friends at school and is often lonely. She sits by herself at lunch because she thinks it's better than being ignored at a table full of people. Paul notices Nina sitting by herself every day. He remembers when he was new at school and didn't have many friends. Paul is sad that Nina is alone. One day he goes to sit with her at lunch.

Intellect—Reason:

_____

_____

Will—Choose:

_____

_____

Emotions—Feel:

_____

_____

Conscience

Part I

Directions: Follow along with your teacher and take notes as instructed.

God gave every human person a conscience. We use our conscience to make moral
decisions: we use our reason to judge the good or evil of an action in light of the
moral law. A well-formed conscience chooses the good; a poorly-formed conscience
may choose wrongly and lead to sin. We have to follow the certain judgment of our
conscience, so we must form our conscience well with God's Word and prayer.

Part II

Directions: Come up with three situations in which our feelings might help us to make the right decisions and three different situations in which our feelings might harm our ability to make good decisions.

Situations in which our feelings may HELP us make the right decision	Situations in which our feelings may HARM our ability to make the right decision
1. _____ _____ _____ _____	1. _____ _____ _____ _____
2. _____ _____ _____ _____	2. _____ _____ _____ _____
3. _____ _____ _____ _____	3. _____ _____ _____ _____

Knowing Truth

Directions: Read the paragraphs below, which are adapted from Pope St. John Paul II's *Fides et Ratio*, nos. 25, 31-33. Then, respond to the questions.

All human beings desire to know. This desire is aimed at discovering the truth. Everyday life shows how concerned each of us is to discover for ourselves, beyond mere opinions, how things really are. ...We are interested in the real truth of what we perceive. ...If we discover something is false, we reject it; but if we can establish truth, we feel rewarded. It is this that Saint Augustine teaches when he writes: "I have met many who wanted to deceive, but none who wanted to be deceived." ...It is essential, therefore, that the values chosen and pursued in one's life be true. Only true values can lead people to fully know themselves and become who they were created to be. You don't find the truth of values by turning in on yourself. You find the truth by opening yourself up to understand the truth even when it goes beyond yourself.

1.   What does Pope St. John Paul II say that human beings want to discover?

   _____

2.   What do humans typically reject? _____

   _____

3.   Where do we find truth?   _____

   _____

Human beings are not made to live alone. They are born into a family, growing there until they enter society. Human beings are born into traditions and language. They receive a range of truths from the culture around them which they believe almost on instinct. ...In the life of the person there are many more truths that are simply believed rather than personally confirmed through experience. Think about it—who could actually assess all the countless scientific findings on which modern life is based? Who could personally examine the flow of information which comes in day after day from all over the world? This information is generally accepted as true. The human being—the one who seeks truth—is also one who lives by belief.

4. List three things you learned from your family that you know are true.

_____

_____

5. Do you think it's possible for one person to double-check every scientific finding or double-check every piece of information that exists on the Internet or on the news? Why or why not?

_____

_____

In believing, we entrust ourselves to the knowledge acquired by other people. This suggests an important tension. On the one hand, knowledge gained through belief can seem imperfect. You may want to perfect it through evidence you personally observe. On the other hand, belief is often richer than just evidence. Belief involves relationship between persons. It uses not only a person's potential to know, but also the deeper ability to trust others – to enter into an enduring relationship.

We see that men and women are on an unstoppable journey of discovery – a search for truth and a search for a person they can trust. The Christian faith comes to meet them, offering the real possibility of reaching the goal they seek. Moving beyond simple belief, the Christian faith enables people to share in the mystery of Christ. Christ offers a true and understandable knowledge of God. In Jesus Christ, who is the Truth, faith recognizes the ultimate appeal to humanity.

6. Why does belief involve a relationship between people?

_____

_____

7. Knowledge of the ultimate truth – God – is something that can be difficult to see on our own. How does Christ help with that?

_____

_____

The Importance of Family

Directions: Read the following excerpts from the *Compendium of the Social Doctrine of the Church*, paragraph 212, then answer the questions that follow. If you are unsure of the meaning of a word, look for the definition in the vocabulary box.

Vocabulary

Climate: the feel of a place.

Communion: the sharing of life with one another.

Conceive: to begin human life in the womb from the union of a man and woman.

Environment: surrounding conditions.

Formative: giving shape to something.

Fundamental: serving as an essential part or basis of something.

Human Ecology: the interdependence of human beings.

Personhood: the state of being a person.

Potentiality: what is possible or could potentially be.

Self: an individual person.

The family has central importance in reference to the person. It is in this cradle of life and love that people are born and grow; when a child is conceived, society receives the gift of a new person who is called "from the innermost depths of self to communion with others and to the giving of self to others."

The Christian family is where children first learn the faith, where parents fulfill their responsibility to teach their children about Jesus, how to pray, and how to help each other get to Heaven.

1. What is a cradle? Why would the Church compare a family to a cradle?

   _____

   _____

   _____

2. Read the definition of the word *conceive*. When does the gift of a person begin?

   _____

   _____

   _____

3. Read the definitions of the words *self* and *communion*. Even though we are individual people, what are we called to?

   _____

   _____

It is in the family, therefore, that the mutual giving of self on the part of man and woman united in marriage creates an environment of life in which children "develop their potentialities, become aware of their dignity and prepare to face their unique and individual destiny."

4. In a family, where does the "gift of self" start? _____

5. Read the definition of *environment*. The Church says the family environment should help children do three things. What are they?

   _____

   _____

6. Read the definition of *potentiality*. What do you think it means to develop *your* potentiality? Why do you think *your* potentiality is unique?

   _____

   _____

7. Try to remember the definition of *dignity* from Lesson 2. What does it mean to be aware of our dignity?

   _____

   _____

8. Think about your own family. How do they prepare you to face the future?

   _____

   _____

In the climate of natural affection, which unites the members of a family unit, persons are recognized and learn responsibility.

9. Read the definition of *climate*. Explain the phrase "climate of natural affection."

   _____

   _____

10. How do you learn responsibility in your family?

   _____

   _____

The first and fundamental structure for "human ecology" is the family, in which man receives his first formative ideas about truth and goodness, and learns what it means to love and to be loved, and thus what it actually means to be a person.

11. Read the definition of *formative*. What do you think it means that we receive our "first formative ideas" from our family?

   _____

   _____

12. Why do you think it's important to learn love in the family?

   _____

   _____

Gospel Skits

Directions: On your own paper, answer the reflection questions about your assigned Gospel story.

The Good Samaritan (Luke 10:25-37)

› What types of people are suffering physically or emotionally in modern times? Who might "pass by" these people?

› How can we be a "gift of self" like the Good Samaritan?

The Healing of the Paralytic (Mark 2:1-12)

› What types of people are suffering physically in modern times?

› Focus on the men carrying the paralytic. How can we be a "gift of self" like them?

The Feeding of the 5,000 (Matthew 14:13-21)

› How can we be a "gift of self" like the boy who donates his bread and fish?

› Although we can't miraculously make bread appear, in what way could we provide for a lot of people at once?

The Parable of the Talents (Matthew 25:14-30)

› Besides money, what are other examples of gifts we have been given?

› How should we use those gifts?

The Washing of the Disciples' Feet (John 13:1-17)

› Think about who Jesus is to the disciples. Place yourself in Jesus' position. Who would the "disciples" be to you?

› In what way can you help your "disciples"?

Gift of Self

Directions: For each skit, write two or three sentences that explain how someone in the skit was a gift of self to a person in need.

The Good Samaritan (Luke 10:25-37)

_____

_____

_____

The Healing of the Paralytic (Mark 2:1-12)

_____

_____

_____

The Feeding of the 5,000 (Matthew 14:13-21)

_____

_____

_____

The Parable of the Talents (Matthew 25:14-30)

_____

_____

_____

The Washing of the Disciples' Feet (John 13:1-17)

_____

_____

_____

Theological Virtues

Directions: Read the following essay on the theological virtues, then answer the questions that follow.

In 2000, during the early days of reality TV, MTV produced a show called Diary. Each episode tracked the daily life of a different celebrity and began with the same voiceover: *You think you know, but you have no idea.* The truth is, no matter how many tell-all interviews we hear, or late-night talk-show appearances we watch, or paparazzi photos we see of a celebrity walking his or her dog, we'll never really know that person. We think we know, we judge the celebrity as if we know, but we really don't know that person. We just know a lot of random things about him or her.

If this is true of our relationship with celebrities, how much truer is it of our relationship with God? It's not a bad thing not to know a lot about God. In fact, since God is infinite, we'll never know everything about Him! But knowing about God is very different from actually knowing Him. This is where **faith** comes in. We read in the *Catechism* that "faith is the theological virtue by which we believe in God and believe all that he has said and revealed to us, and that Holy Church proposes for our belief, because he is truth itself" (CCC 1814). The best way to come to know God is through trusting in His revelation of Himself. More than just a list of facts about Him, God reveals His love for us, and enters into a relationship with us. We might think we know who God is because we know a lot about Him, but the only way we can truly know Him is if, through the virtue of

faith, we trust Him and who He has revealed Himself to be.

The Church has preserved Divine Revelation through Scripture, Sacred Tradition, and the Magisterium, the Church's teaching authority. God's revelation of Himself is clearest in the person of Jesus Christ. St. John the Evangelist writes that God "became flesh and made his dwelling among us, and we saw his glory" (John 1:14). God assumed a human nature in Jesus Christ. He is "the light [that] shines in the darkness, and the darkness has not overcome it" (John 1:5). In the darkness of our world, Jesus is the light. And He reveals the Father to us in a way that no other revelation of God can surpass.

Hope is "the theological virtue by which we desire the kingdom of heaven and eternal life as our happiness, placing our trust in Christ's promises and relying not on our own strength, but on the help of the grace of the Holy Spirit" (CCC 1817). Jesus promised us that He would remain with us "always, until the end of the age" (Matthew 28:20). With the virtue of hope, we can trust in a steadfast God who gives us the grace to become the people He has created and called us to be.

Charles Schulz, the creator of the Peanuts comics, wrote, "I love mankind ... it's people I can't stand!" It can be easy to say, "We need to love everyone," but do we remember that line every time we interact with someone? Sometimes people are difficult to love. When we choose to be impatient or rude or cruel to another person, however, our actions show that we don't really understand what **love** is, when it is looked at as a virtue. It is "the theological virtue by which we love God above all things for his own sake, and our neighbor as ourselves for the love of God" (CCC 1822). Loving God gives us the grace and the strength we need to love the people in our lives, especially when it's difficult to do so. When we love God as our Father, we remember that every person is our brother or sister. This virtue helps us to choose what is best for everyone in our lives; it strengthens our relationship with God and helps us to treat others with the respect and kindness they deserve.

1. Why can't we know a celebrity from watching him or her on TV?

    _____

2. What is the virtue of faith? _____

    _____

3. What is the best way to know God? _____

    _____

4. Through what has the Church preserved divine revelation?

    _____

5. How is God's revelation of Himself made clearest? _____

    _____

6. What is the virtue of hope? _____

    _____

7. What did Jesus promise us? _____

8. What does the virtue of hope allow us to do? _____

    _____

9. What is the virtue of love? _____

    _____

10. What does loving God give us the grace and the strength to do?

    _____

    _____

    _____

Reflection Question

Why are the virtues of faith, hope, and love essential for us to know God? How can you strengthen these virtues in your life so that you can know God better?

_____

_____

_____

_____

_____

_____

_____

Types of Prayer

Prayer of Adoration

Adoration is a form of prayer in which we worship God and express our love for Him.

Prayer in Praise of God, St. Francis of Assisi

You are holy, Lord, the only God,
and Your deeds are wonderful.
You are strong.
You are great.
You are the Most High.
You are Almighty.
You, Holy Father, are King of heaven and
earth.
You are Three and One, Lord God, all Good.
You are Good, all Good, supreme Good, Lord
God, living and true.
You are love. You are wisdom.
You are humility. You are endurance.

You are rest. You are peace.
You are joy and gladness.
You are justice and moderation.
You are all our riches, and You suffice for us.
You are beauty.
You are gentleness.
You are our protector.
You are our guardian and defender.
You are our courage. You are our haven and
our hope.
You are our faith, our great consolation.
You are our eternal life, Great and Wonderful
Lord, God Almighty, Merciful Savior.

Prayer of Thanksgiving

Thanksgiving is a form of prayer that shows gratitude to God for every gift.

> Bless the LORD, my soul; and do not forget all his gifts. –PSALM 103:2

> All good giving and every perfect gift is from above, coming down from the Father of lights, with whom there is no alteration or shadow caused by change. –JAMES 1:17

Prayer of Contrition

Contrition is the experience of sorrow for sins and the resolve not to sin again. Perfect contrition arises out of love for God. Imperfect contrition is sorrow we experience for other reasons, such as disgust for the sin, or the fear of punishment. Prayers of contrition ask God for His mercy.

Examination of Conscience

Our Father, who art in heaven, hallowed be
Thy name.

› Do I give time to God every day in prayer?

› Do I pay attention and participate during
Mass every Sunday?

› Have I used the names of God or Jesus in
anger or disrespectfully?

Thy kingdom come; Thy will be done on earth
as it is in heaven.

› Am I kind to others?

› Do I do what Jesus wants me to do?

› Do I share with others?

› Am I helpful to my family and neighbors?

- Do I set a good example for others, particularly those younger than I am?
- Do I show respect to my parents, teachers, and classmates?

Give us this day our daily bread.
- Am I thankful for the good things in my life?
- Am I ever greedy or jealous of others?
- Do I make an effort to help those who have no food, clothes, shelter, or money?
- Do I take things that don't belong to me?
- Have I destroyed or misused another person's property intentionally or through carelessness?

Forgive us our trespasses as we forgive those who trespass against us.
- Do I say I'm sorry when I have been wrong?

- Do I forgive and forget when someone does something that offends me, or do I hold a grudge?
- Do I help solve problems between my friends, or do I cause more trouble?
- Do I say bad or unkind things about people, either behind their back or directly to hurt their feelings?

And lead us not into temptation, but deliver us from evil.
- Do I play fairly in sports and games?
- Am I honest in my schoolwork?
- Do I tell the truth?
- Do I treat my body and other people's bodies with purity and respect?
- Do I look at TV shows, movies, or pictures that are morally wrong?
- Do I let other kids tempt me to do things I know I shouldn't do? Do I tempt others?

Act of Contrition

We pray the Act of Contrition after we have confessed our sins to a priest in the Sacrament of Penance and Reconciliation. The priest forgives our sins in the Person of Christ, and we are reconciled to God and the Church.

Act of Contrition Prayer

O my God, I am sorry with all my heart for having offended you, and I detest all my sins because of your just punishments, but most of all because they offend you, my God, who are all good and deserving of all my love. I firmly resolve, with the help of your grace, to sin no more and to avoid whatever leads me to sin. Amen.

Prayer of Intercession

Intercession is a form of prayer in which we ask for God's help for others.

Because he clings to me I will deliver him; because he knows my name I will set him on high. He will call upon me and I will answer; I will be with him in distress; I will deliver him.
—PSALM 91:14-15

Gifts of the Holy Spirit

Directions: Read the information below and use it to complete the chart that follows.

When we are baptized, we receive the Holy Spirit. God invites each of us to participate in His power and grace. The Bible talks about very specific ways this grace is given to us in our lives. We call these graces *the Gifts of the Holy Spirit*. The prophet Isaiah talks about seven of these gifts. Let's explore these gifts a little more.

The beginning of true *wisdom* is a respect and love for God. This gift is more than giving good advice. Wisdom perfects our faith, because it helps us to see God for who He is. When our faith is inspired by a real love for God, our lives will never be the same!

The gift of *fear of the Lord* does not mean being terrified by something scary. Another word for fear is "awe" or "wonder." This gift inspires us to see God as He is, not who we think He might be, and to be in awe of His glory and might. We recognize that He is majestic, powerful, and all loving; that He is truth, beauty, and goodness. When we see God for who He is, we know in our hearts that we must avoid sin, and our relationship with Him is strengthened.

As we grow in our relationship with God, the gift of *piety* helps us to know God as our Father. Piety is to have reverence for holy things and for God. This gift helps us to have the right attitude toward God and to worship Him because we love Him.

Our Catholic Faith contains many different teachings. These teachings aren't always easy to understand! The gift of *understanding* helps us know and understand the truths of our Faith that are beyond our ability to know by ourselves. God's grace helps us to get to the heart of the truth and to know and follow God's will for us.

The Holy Spirit's gift of *knowledge* isn't knowing all the right answers on a test. Rather, this gift helps us to see things through God's eyes. It makes it easier to distinguish between truth and temptation. The gift of knowledge helps us to know God's plan for our lives and to act upon it. Knowledge helps us to overcome our weaknesses, sins, and failures. When we see how God is moving in our lives, we can see how both the good things and the bad things have a purpose and meaning.

God gives to us the gift of *fortitude* for the times we face challenges in life. With this gift, we're able to overcome the difficulties, pain, and suffering in our lives with energy and resolve. We are strengthened to stand up for and defend the Catholic Faith even to the point of physical harm or death. With this gift we are able to do God's will in our lives and our fear is removed.

The gift of *counsel* or right judgment helps us to be more open to what our conscience is saying. It helps us to know right from wrong and to judge whether things will lead us toward God or away from Him.

The Gifts of the Holy Spirit are very real graces that we can pray and ask God for. God wants to give them to us! Through these gifts, we receive help in our daily life to deepen our faith, make good decisions, and treat others well. God wants to change our lives for the better. Let us open our hearts to receive His gifts and His love.

Gifts of the Holy Spirit.	From whom do we receive the gift?	What is the gift? (Define each in your own words.)	How does it help?
1 Wisdom			
2 Understanding			
3 Counsel			

Gifts of the Holy Spirit.	From whom do we receive the gift?	What is the gift? (Define each in your own words.)	How does it help?
4 Fortitude			
5 Knowledge			
6 Piety			
7 Fear of the Lord			

Cardinal Virtues

Directions: Read about each cardinal virtue, and then write an example of how you could practice that virtue in your life.

A virtue is "a habitual and firm disposition to do good" (CCC 1833). A disposition is an interior tendency. Thus, a virtue is an interior tendency to do the good. We possess a virtue when we've developed an instinctive habit of doing the right thing. The word *cardinal* comes from the Latin *cardo*, meaning "hinge." Think about the hinge on a door: it connects the door to the frame. It helps the door stay put and allows it to open and close. The cardinal virtues are similar: many other virtues "hinge" on them. They help us continually do the good and to choose what is right.

The cardinal virtues help to connect our decisions to the grace of God. When we possess the cardinal virtues, we're able to "stay put" in God's grace. Virtues also help us to fulfill the purpose for which we were made: holiness! Each of the cardinal virtues plays an important role in our life.

Prudence comes first. Prudence means right reason in action. Prudence helps guide all of the other virtues because it helps us to discern the true good in every circumstance. Prudence helps us to make the right decision at the right time. It helps us to find the best way to achieve a good outcome.

1. What is an example of a situation in which you could practice prudence in your life?

_____

_____

_____

_____

Temperance helps us seek the right amount of good things. Have you ever known somebody who ate too many desserts? It's okay have dessert every once in a while, but we know that overeating will not be good for our health. And we know that not eating enough food will also harm us. The virtue of temperance helps us to find a balance between too much and too little of the good things in life. Temperance often requires us to restrain our desires, and is sometimes called moderation. Chastity is a fruit of the Holy Spirit that flows from temperance.

2. What is an example of a situation in which you could practice temperance in your life?

_____

_____

_____

The word "justice" seems to be used in many different ways today. It may make you think of the police, or courtrooms, or even superheroes. But justice is about more than fighting crime. *Justice* is the virtue that helps us give God and neighbor their due. Remember that every human being is created in the image and likeness of God. That means that every person—from conception to their natural death—has dignity and is due respect. Being truthful is also part of being just and showing love to our neighbor. Being true means not only telling the truth, but having integrity in what you say and what you do. Our actions must be consistent with our words. We must not hide the truth if our intent is to trick or deceive someone. Saying false things about others with the intent of harming their reputation is called calumny. Being kind, truthful, and charitable to others is not only "being nice," it is true justice.

3. What is an example of a situation in which you could practice justice in your life?

_____

_____

_____

Sometimes making the right decision is easy. Have you ever wanted to help someone just because you saw that the person needed it? Maybe you comforted your friend when he was sad or helped your sister with a chore because it was too much for her to do alone. Sometimes making the right decision is more challenging, such as standing up to someone who is bullying someone else when the bully could hurt you too. The virtue of fortitude helps in these situations. *Fortitude* involves "persevering in what is right." To persevere means to continue in the face of difficulty. Fortitude helps us to keep going when times get tough. In real trials, fortitude helps us endure persecution and even face death for a just cause.

4. What is an example of a situation in which you could practice fortitude in your life?

_____

_____

_____

Spiritual Superhero

Directions: Create your own spiritual superhero based on your assigned gift of the Holy Spirit or virtue. Then answer the following questions.

What is the name of your spiritual superhero?

_____

What is your spiritual superhero's ability or power? (Be sure it directly relates to your assigned gift or virtue.)

_____

_____

_____

Create a brief backstory for your superhero. Why does this particular gift of the Holy Spirit or virtue mean so much to him or her? (Be sure to show evidence of your understanding of your assigned gift or virtue.)

_____

_____

_____

_____

_____

_____

_____

How does your spiritual superhero use his or her ability or power to help other people?

_____

_____

_____

_____

_____

_____

What other unique tools, equipment, or sidekicks help your spiritual superhero carry out his or her mission?

_____

_____

_____

_____

_____

_____

On a separate piece of paper, draw a picture of your spiritual superhero using his or her ability or power to help others.

How God Sees Us

Directions: Look up and read each Scripture passage listed below and decide what each says about our human dignity – how God sees us. Write a sentence or two that describes what each passage says about our human dignity.

1. Psalm 139:13-14 _____

   _____

2. Proverbs 22:2 _____

   _____

3. 1 Corinthians 3:16 _____

   _____

4. 1 John 3:1 _____

   _____

5. Jeremiah 1:5 _____

   _____

6. Psalm 8:5-6 _____

   _____

7. Isaiah 49:16 _____

   _____

8. Romans 5:8 _____

   _____

My Gifts

Directions: Read the parable of the talents, then answer the questions that follow in complete sentences.

Matthew 25:14-30

It will be as when a man who was going on a journey called in his servants and entrusted his possessions to them. To one he gave five talents; to another, two; to a third, one – to each according to his ability. Then he went away. Immediately the one who received five talents went and traded with them, and made another five. Likewise, the one who received two made another two. But the man who received one went off and dug a hole in the ground and buried his master's money. After a long time the master of those servants came back and settled accounts with them. The one who had received five talents came forward bringing the additional five. He said, "Master, you gave me five talents. See, I have made five more." His master said to him, "Well done, my good and faithful servant. Since you were faithful in small matters, I will give you great responsibilities. Come, share your master's joy." [Then] the one who had received two talents also came forward and said, "Master, you gave me two talents. See, I have made two more." His master said to him, "Well done, my good and faithful servant. Since you were faithful in small matters, I will give you great responsibilities. Come, share your master's joy." Then the one who had received the one talent came forward and said, "Master, I knew you were a demanding person, harvesting where you did not plant and gathering where you did not scatter; so out of fear I went off and buried your talent in the ground. Here it is back." His master said to him in reply, "You wicked, lazy servant! So you knew that I harvest where I did not plant and gather where I did not scatter? Should you not then have put my money in the bank so that I could have got it back with interest on my return? Now then! Take the talent from him and give it to the one with ten. For to everyone who has, more will be given and he will grow rich; but from the one who has not, even what he has will be taken away. And throw this useless servant into the darkness outside, where there will be wailing and grinding of teeth."

1. Which of the servants in the parable do you feel is most like you? Why?

   _____

   _____

   _____

   _____

2. If God were to ask you right now how you have used the "talents" or gifts He has given you, how would you be able to respond? Have you used your God-given gifts to honor God and help others? Why or why not?

_____

_____

_____

_____

3. What are two gifts that God has given you that you can use for others?

_____

_____

_____

_____

4. Describe at least two specific ways that you can use each gift you listed above to help others?

_____

_____

_____

_____

UNIT 2

Jesus and the Gospel Message

In this unit, you will learn about...

> Divine Revelation and its written record in the Old and New Testaments.

> The inspiration and authorship of Scripture.

> The formation of the Gospels and their literary aspects.

> The world of the New Testament.

> The Incarnation.

> Jesus' life, Passion, Death, and Resurrection.

> The four Gospels: Matthew, Mark, Luke, and John.

Introduction

Sacred Scripture is the written record of God's revelation of Himself. Throughout Salvation History God revealed Himself to His Chosen People and made known His loving plan of mercy and salvation. This revelation culminated in the Incarnation, when the Son of God assumed a human nature in the Person of Jesus Christ. In Him, God has said all that needs to be said for the sake of our salvation. Jesus is God's one, perfect, and unsurpassable Word.

All of Scripture is inspired by God. This means that God, working in and through the Holy Spirit, moved through the human authors of Scripture to write what He wanted committed to writing. God is, therefore, the primary author of Scripture, however, the human writers are also true authors who wrote using their own powers and abilities. In order for us to properly interpret Scripture, then, we must consider not only the intention of the human authors, but the various truths God wanted known for the sake of our salvation. The Church, in her wisdom, guides our interpretation of the truth.

At the heart of the Scriptures are the Gospels, which contain the Good News of salvation in Jesus Christ. In them, we encounter Christ Himself, the Word of God made flesh, who fulfills all of God's promises throughout Salvation History. All of Jesus' life teaches us. We learn not just from what He said, but from what He did. And of course, we learn from Him the greatest truth of all: God loved the world so much that He gave His Son so that those who believe in Him could have everlasting lift. Jesus – God the Son – came down from Heaven, assumed a human nature, and died to take away our sins. He rose again, defeating death and opening Heaven to us. This is what we mean when we say Jesus Christ is the fullness of all Revelation. Because He is true God and true man, Jesus is the one and only mediator between God and humanity. A mediator is someone who makes peace between two parties. So to say that Jesus is the only mediator means that only Jesus brings us back into friendship with the Father. The Bible tells us, "For there is one God. There is also one mediator between God and the human race, Christ Jesus, himself human, who gave himself as ransom for all" (1 Timothy 2:5). He established a New Covenant by His Paschal Mystery, His Passion, Death, and Resurrection, which defeated sin and death and won for us new life as sons and daughters of God. Reading the Gospels also reminds us that the Resurrection is a real historical event, witnessed and testified to by real people: the disciples, who encountered our Risen Lord. We participate in Christ's sacrifice when we receive the Eucharist at Mass and we enter into His Paschal Mystery in our daily lives. The Gospels, then, are our primary source of knowledge of Jesus, and His saving actions.

Are there any questions you still have about the topics you learned last month? What steps can you take to find out the answers?

_____

_____

_____

_____

What questions do you have right now about the topics you will be learning about in this unit?

_____

_____

_____

_____

Unit 2 Vocabulary

Annunciation: The Gospel story of the Angel Gabriel appearing to Mary to announce that she would be the Mother of God, Jesus Christ. The Church celebrates this feast every year on March 25th. The Gospel story of the Annunciation can be found in Luke 1:26-38.

Apostle: A person who is sent out as a representative of someone else. Jesus chose twelve men to be His Apostles. They preached Jesus' message of salvation and worked miracles in His name. Jesus gave the Apostles special authority and made them the first leaders (bishops) of the Church.

Apostolic Succession: The handing on of apostolic preaching and authority from the Apostles to their successors the bishops through the laying on of hands, as a permanent office in the Church. The fourth mark of the Church is that the Church is apostolic, which means that the Church is built on the lasting foundation of the Apostles.

Canon of Scripture: The official list of inspired books that appear in the Bible. The Catholic canon of Scripture includes 46 Old Testament books and 27 New Testament books.

Covenant: A sacred permanent bond of family relationship. God entered into a series of covenants with mankind throughout Salvation History to invite us to be part of His divine family and to prepare gradually and in stages and in words and deeds to receive the gift of salvation.

Divine Revelation: The body of truths revealed to us by God throughout Salvation History.

Evangelist: One of the four Gospel writers, who wrote with the purpose of evangelizing, or to share the Good News of Jesus Christ with the world.

Exorcism: One of the types of miracles that Jesus performed, in which He cast out demons that had possessed people. Jesus gave to His Apostles the authority to cast out demons in His name.

Gentiles: People of non-Jewish ethnicity.

Gospel: "Good News." The four Gospels are the heart of the Scriptures and proclaim the Good News of salvation won for us by the Passion, Death, and Resurrection of Jesus Christ. The Gospels are our primary source of knowledge of the life of Jesus Christ.

Hanukkah: Jewish holiday that celebrates the purification of the Jerusalem Temple at the end of the Maccabean Revolt, around 150 years before the birth of Christ. The ancient Greeks had taken over Jerusalem, forcibly made the Jewish people adopt Greek customs, and rededicated the Temple to Zeus. A group of Jewish rebels known as the Maccabees successfully defeated the Greeks and reclaimed Jerusalem and the Temple.

Hasmonean Dynasty: A new line of Jewish kings established to rule Israel after the Maccabean revolt. The Hasmonean kings were not descended from David and thus were not the heirs to God's Old Testament promises. The Hasmoneans ruled Israel until 63 BC when the Romans took over.

Incarnation: The Christian belief that the second Person of the Holy Trinity, the Son of God, assumed a human nature in the Person of Jesus Christ.

Inerrant: Without error. Scripture teaches solidly, faithfully, and without error the truth God wanted known for the sake of our salvation.

Inspiration: The human authors of Scripture were guided by God through the Holy Spirit in their writing. God's Spirit was present with them when they chose the words to write and how to write them. The Holy Spirit moved within them to write the truth God wanted written for the sake of our salvation.

Kingdom of God: God's reign or rule over all things. During His public ministry, Jesus proclaimed that the Kingdom of God was at hand. The Church is the seed, or beginning, of the Kingdom here on earth. The Kingdom will be fulfilled in Heaven.

Literary Genres of the Bible: The various writing styles that appear in Scripture. These include narrative, law, prophecy, poetry, wisdom writings or proverbs, parables, genealogy or ancestries, epistles or letters, and apocalyptic writing.

Magisterium: The teaching authority of the Church and those who exercise that authority, the pope and all of the world's bishops in union with the pope. The Magisterium of the Church authentically teaches and interprets the Word of God so that the faithful might be saved.

Messiah: The Hebrew word for "anointed one." All of the kings descended from David were anointed as a sign of their kingship. This made all of the kings in the line of David "messiahs." God promised the Chosen People that He would send the Messiah to free them from sin. Jesus is the Son of David and God's promised Messiah and Savior.

Miracle: A supernatural act of God that demonstrates His power over all things. Jesus performed many miracles because He is God. Jesus' miracles invited people to believe in Him and showed the power of God. Jesus' miracles were also signs of the Kingdom of God.

Mystery: A truth about God that we can come to know only with God's help.

Paschal Mystery: Christ's Passion, Death, and Resurrection which saved us from sin and death for new life as sons and daughters of God.

Pentateuch: The Greek name for the first five books of the Old Testament: Genesis, Exodus, Leviticus, Numbers, and Deuteronomy. Also known as the Books of Moses.

Pharisee: A member of a powerful group of leaders in Jewish society during the time of Jesus. They believed that in order for Israel to remain faithful to God, the people must remain pure and hold strictly to the Law of Moses. They exaggerated the law and customs to the point that they became burdens and refused to associate with Gentiles. They rejected the belief that Jerusalem would be an everlasting kingdom and center of worship for all the nations. Like Jesus, they believed in the afterlife and resurrection of the body.

Roman Peace: A time of relative peace and stability throughout the Roman Empire. It was during this time that Jesus was born. Also called the "*Pax Romana.*"

Sacred Scripture: The written record of God's revelation of Himself. It is the speech of God put down in writing under the breath of the Holy Spirit. The Word of God.

Sacred Tradition: The mode of transmission of the Word of God. The Word of God was given to the Apostles by Jesus and the Holy Spirit. The Apostles in turn handed it on to their successors, the bishops. With the help of the Holy Spirit, the Church has kept the Word of God whole and safe over the centuries so we can know and believe in the whole Faith today. Sacred Tradition and Sacred Scripture make up a single deposit – or one gift – of the Word of God. We accept and honor Sacred Tradition equally with Sacred Scripture.

Sadducee: A member of a powerful group of leaders in Jewish society who believed the only way for the Jewish faith to survive was for the people to cooperate with the Gentiles. They believed that only the Pentateuch was canonical Scripture and rejected traditional interpretations and later additions to the Law and covenants contained in Scripture (specifically the covenant with David). Unlike Jesus, they did not believe in the afterlife, the resurrection of the body, or supernatural beings such as angels.

Salvation History: The story of God's love and mercy revealed to us throughout human history, culminating in Christ's sacrifice on the Cross and Resurrection from the dead, which won for us salvation from sin and death.

Synoptic: "To see together." The Gospels of Matthew, Mark, and Luke are known as the Synoptic Gospels because they present the story of Christ's life in a similar way and even borrow stories and the structure of their Gospels from each other.

The Senses of Scripture: The Senses of Scripture: The meanings of Scripture and the events described in it. There are two senses of Scripture: literal and spiritual. The literal sense is the meaning of the words of Scripture discovered by study of the text. The spiritual sense allows us to understand that, thanks to the unity of God's plan, the realities and events the text describes are themselves signs of our Faith. For example, the parting of the Red Sea is a sign of Baptism. The fullness of God's plan of revelation is revealed in Christ. All interpretation of Scripture must be guided by the judgment of the Church, which has the responsibility of protecting and interpreting the Word of God. The unity of the literal and spiritual senses allow the Church to interpret the riches of Sacred Scripture.

Typology: The study of "types." Typology studies how one thing leaves an imprint on a later thing in Salvation History. The earlier thing is a "type." The study of types is most often considered in relation to Jesus Christ and the events of salvation.

Visitation: The Gospel story of Mary's visit to her cousin Elizabeth shortly after the Angel Gabriel had appeared to Mary to announce the Incarnation. At their meeting, the child in Elizabeth's womb, John the Baptist, leapt for joy in the presence of the unborn Jesus.

Vocation: The calling or destiny of all people in this life and the next. God first calls everyone to love and serve Him and to seek the perfection of holiness. God also calls each person to a state of life: either marriage, religious life, or ordained priesthood. The Church offers special care to those single persons who find themselves in circumstances not of their own choosing.

Word of God: A title for Jesus Christ and a title for Sacred Scripture. Jesus is the Word of God become flesh in the Incarnation. In Him, God has revealed all that is necessary for the sake of our salvation. We meet Jesus in Sacred Scripture, the Word of God written down to preserve and communicate the Good News of salvation.

Christ the Redeemer Statue
BY PAUL LANDOWSKI (C. 1931)

Corcovado Mountain, Tijuca Forest National Park. Rio de Janeiro, Brazil.

Christic the Redeemer Statue

Christ the Redeemer, *by Paul Landowski* (c. 1931)

Directions: Take some time to quietly view and reflect on the art. Let yourself be inspired in any way that happens naturally. Then think about the questions below, and discuss them with your classmates.

Conversation Questions

1. How would you describe how Jesus looks in this statue? How does His appearance add to your understanding of who Jesus is and what He is like?

2. In what shape is Jesus standing in this statue?

3. Read Mark 12:28-34. In what two ways does Jesus command us to love? How would you put Jesus' two commandments of love in your own words?

> One of the scribes, when he came forward and heard them disputing and saw how well he had answered them, asked him, "Which is the first of all the commandments?" Jesus replied, "The first is this: 'Hear, O Israel! The Lord our God is Lord alone! You shall love the Lord your God with all your heart, with all your soul, with all your mind, and with all your strength.' The second is this: 'You shall love your neighbor as yourself.' There is no other commandment greater than these." The scribe said to him, "Well said, teacher. You are right in saying, 'He is One and there is no other than he.' And 'to love him with all your heart, with all your understanding, with all your strength, and to love your neighbor as yourself' is worth more than all burnt offerings and sacrifices." And when Jesus saw that [he] answered with understanding, he said to him, "You are not far from the kingdom of God." And no one dared to ask him any more questions.

4. What did the scribe in Mark 12:28-34 say that following these commands was worth more than?

5. The *Catechism of the Catholic Church* no. 1766 tells us that "to love is to will the good of another." How would you put this in your own words?

6. Read *Catechism of the Catholic Church* no. 1825:

> Christ died out of love for us, while we were still "enemies." The Lord asks us to love as he does, even our *enemies*, to make ourselves the neighbor of those farthest away,

and to love children and the poor as Christ himself. The Apostle Paul has given an incomparable depiction of charity: "charity is patient and kind, charity is not jealous or boastful; it is not arrogant or rude. Charity does not insist on its own way; it is not irritable or resentful; it does not rejoice at wrong, but rejoices in the right. Charity bears all things, believes all things, hopes all things, endures all things."

Charity is the virtue by which we follow Jesus in loving God above all and loving our neighbors as ourselves. What does this passage from the *Catechism* tell us about how charity helps us imitate Jesus' love?

7. Jesus' two commandments of love can be visualized in the Cross: the love between God and each of us on the vertical line, and our love for each other on the horizontal line. How did Jesus show both loves on the Cross?

8. How does Jesus' Death on the Cross deepen your understanding of what it means to love God and love our neighbors?

Heroes of Faith: Abraham and Mary

Directions: Read the Scripture passages below, then answer the questions that follow.

Genesis 12:1-5

The LORD said to Abram: "Go forth from your land, your relatives, and from your father's house to a land that I will show you. I will make of you a great nation, and I will bless you; I will make your name great, so that you will be a blessing. I will bless those who bless you and curse those who curse you. All the families of the earth will find blessing in you." Abram went as the LORD directed him, and Lot went with him. Abram was seventy-five years old when he left Haran. Abram took his wife Sarai, his brother's son Lot, all the possessions that they had accumulated, and the persons they had acquired in Haran, and they set out for the land of Canaan.

Genesis 22:1-14

Some time afterward, God put Abraham to the test and said to him: "Abraham!" "Here I am!" he replied. Then God said: "Take your son Isaac, your only one, whom you love, and go to the land of Moriah. There offer him up as a burnt offering on one of the heights that I will point out to you." Early the next morning Abraham saddled his donkey, took with him two of his servants and his son Isaac, and after cutting the wood for the burnt offering, set out for the place of which God had told him.

On the third day Abraham caught sight of the place from a distance. Abraham said to his servants: "Stay here with the donkey, while the boy and I go on over there. We will worship and then come back to you."

So Abraham took the wood for the burnt offering and laid it on his son Isaac, while he himself carried the fire and the knife. As the two walked on together, Isaac spoke to his father Abraham. "Father!" he said. "Here I am," he replied. Isaac continued, "Here are the fire and the wood, but where is the sheep for the burnt offering?" "My son," Abraham answered, "God will provide the sheep for the burnt offering." Then the two walked on together. When they came to the place of which God had told him, Abraham built an altar there and arranged the wood on it. Next he bound his son Isaac, and put him on top of the wood on the altar. Then Abraham reached out and took the knife to slaughter his son. But the angel of the LORD called to him from heaven, "Abraham, Abraham!" "Here I am," he answered. "Do not lay your hand on the boy," said the angel. "Do not do the least thing to him. For now I know that you fear God, since you did not withhold from me your son, your only one." Abraham looked up and saw a single ram caught by its horns in the thicket. So Abraham went and took the ram and offered it up as a burnt offering in place of his son. Abraham named that place Yahweh-yireh; hence people today say, "On the mountain the LORD will provide."

Luke 1:26-38

In the sixth month, the angel Gabriel was sent from God to a town of Galilee called Nazareth, to a virgin betrothed to a man named Joseph, of the house of David, and the virgin's name was Mary. And coming to her, he said, "Hail, favored one! The Lord is with you." But she was greatly troubled at what was said and pondered what sort of greeting this might be. Then the angel said to her, "Do not be afraid, Mary, for you have found favor with God. Behold, you will conceive in your womb and bear a son, and you shall name him Jesus. He will be great and will be called Son of the Most High, and the Lord God will give him the throne of David his father, and he will rule over the house of Jacob forever, and of his kingdom there will be no end." But Mary said to the angel, "How can this be, since I have no relations with a man?" And the angel said to her in reply, "The holy Spirit will come upon you, and the power of the Most High will overshadow you. Therefore the child to be born will be called holy, the Son of God. And behold, Elizabeth, your relative, has also conceived a son in her old age, and this is the sixth month for her who was called barren; for nothing will be impossible for God." Mary said, "Behold, I am the handmaid of the Lord. May it be done to me according to your word." Then the angel departed from her.

1. How does Abraham exemplify the virtue of faith? _____

_____

2. How does Mary exemplify the virtue of faith? _____

_____

3. The *Catechism* calls Abraham the Father of Faith. Why is this a fitting title for him?

_____

4. The *Catechism* calls Mary the perfect embodiment of faith. Why is this a fitting way to describe her?

_____

5. Faith is not simply a blind leap. How did Abraham and Mary both make informed decisions that lead them to submit to faith?

_____

6. The *Catechism* says that faith is a gift but also a human act that requires our response. How can it be both? Explain this in light of the examples of Abraham and Mary.

_____

_____

7. What can you learn from the examples of Abraham and Mary that will help you more fully respond to God in faith?

_____

An Informed Faith: Scripture and Tradition

Directions: Read the essay, then answer the questions that follow.

In paragraph 150, the *Catechism of the Catholic Church* states: "Faith is first of all a personal adherence of man to God. At the same time, and inseparably, it is a *free assent to the whole truth that God has revealed.*" In other words, faith is not just a blind leap but an informed decision. Faith requires the use of our intellect and our will. Where can we discover this truth that God has revealed in order to be able to assent to it?

If we take a closer look at human history, we will discover that there has never been a culture or civilization that did not have some notion of religion. In other words, we discover that the human person yearns for answers. The human person yearns for the infinite. We yearn for something outside ourselves and for the divine. Most religions are all about our search for God and the divine. Christianity, however, is about God's search for man. In other words, if we pay attention and look closely, we don't have to try very hard to find God. We will discover that He is searching for us and has left us clues to help us encounter Him. Throughout human history God has been active. He has revealed Himself to us in a variety of ways.

The first way we can come to know God is through His creation: the world and the human person. If we look around at the natural created world we can come to the conclusion that something greater than us designed it. The world and everything in it, including us, are complex, beautiful, and well ordered. This leads us to know that there is a designer behind all of this and us.

The second way we can see that God has revealed Himself to us is through the two pillars of divine revelation. Divine revelation is the body of truths shown to us by God. The two pillars of divine revelation are Sacred Scripture and Sacred Tradition. Sacred Scripture is the inspired word of God written down and passed on to us throughout history. Sacred Tradition is the mode of transmission of the Word of God. The Word of God was given to the Apostles by Jesus and the Holy Spirit. The Apostles in turn handed it on to their successors, the bishops. With the help of the Holy Spirit, the Church has kept the Word of God whole and safe over the centuries so we can know and believe in the whole Faith today. Scripture and Tradition are inherently linked. The Dogmatic Constitution on Divine Revelation states, "Both Scripture and Tradition must be accepted with equal sentiments of reverence and devotion" (9). Scripture and Tradition together make up what we call the Deposit of Faith. The Deposit of Faith is the entirety of what we believe.

The Process of Divine Revelation: A Summary

God has communicated Himself to us gradually. Scripture is the story of God's gradual revelation to man. At the beginning of time, God revealed Himself through His creation. He revealed Himself to Adam and

Eve in a very personal way in the Garden of Eden. After the Fall of Man, God did not abandon His people; He continued to reveal Himself to them. He began with Noah, then continued with Abraham, Moses, David, and the prophets. God worked through these people to prepare humanity for the coming of His Son. In the fullness of time, God sent His Son to save us and complete His Revelation. Jesus Christ became the mediator between God and man. He is the fullness of all revelation.

Revelation has been handed down to us through the Apostles. It has been handed on in two ways: orally and in writing. This is continued today through Apostolic Succession. Apostolic Succession is the process by which, beginning with the Apostles, men are ordained to carry on the mission of Christ here on Earth. We call these men bishops. The Twelve Apostles were the first bishops of the Church. Every bishop in the Church can be traced back in a direct line to one of the Twelve Apostles. Bishops then ordain priests to help them carry out their mission. Bishops have been entrusted with handing on and teaching about God's revelation to us. The bishops in union with the Pope, who is the Bishop of Rome, make up the teaching authority of the Church, which is called the Magisterium. The Magisterium is responsible for guarding and handing on the Deposit of Faith.

Conclusion

Knowing all this, then, it is up to us whether we will respond in faith. The *Catechism of the Catholic Church* no. 27 states, "The desire for God is written in the human heart, because man is created by God and for God; and God never ceases to draw man to himself." St. Augustine states, "You have made us for yourself O Lord, and our hearts are restless until they rest in you." Once we recognize and understand that God has revealed Himself, we must respond. To respond in faith is to submit our intellect and our wills to God. This is something that takes effort and understanding. It is not something based in our own understanding or something we leap into blindly. Responding in faith requires us to be informed. How do we become informed? We search, study, and come to see the ways God has revealed Himself through Sacred Scripture and Sacred Tradition!

1. Faith requires use of our _____ and _____.

2. Religion is about _____ search for _____. Christianity is

   about _____ search for _____.

3. What is the first way we can come to know/discover God?

   _____

4. What are the two pillars of divine revelation?

   _____

5. Of the two pillars of divine revelation, which is more important?

   _____

6. How has this revelation been handed on to us? _____

   _____

7. What is Apostolic Succession? _____

   _____

8. Who are the successors of the Apostles? _____

9. Why do you think Apostolic Succession would be important for the handing on of the Faith?

   _____

   _____

10. If one comes to the conclusion that everything revealed in the Scriptures and everything handed on through Tradition is true, what is the only logical response? Why is this response so difficult to make?

   _____

   _____

   _____

   _____

Divine Revelation Quiz

Directions: Complete the following quiz without use of notes or help from your neighbor.

1. What are the two main sources of divine revelation?

    _____

    _____

2. Who is the fullness of all revelation? _____

3. What is the Magisterium? _____

4. Who are the successors of the Apostles? _____

5. Briefly summarize how divine revelation has been handed on.

    _____

    _____

    _____

The Evangelist Matthew Inspired by an Angel
BY REMBRANDT (1661)

The Louvre-Lens, Lens, Pas-de-Calais, Northern France.

Understanding Divine Inspiration

Directions: Read the excerpt from *Dogmatic Constitution on Divine Revelation* (*Dei Verbum* 11-13), then complete the questions that follow.

CHAPTER III
Sacred Scripture, Its Inspiration and Divine Interpretation

11. Those divinely revealed realities which are contained and presented in Sacred Scripture have been committed to writing under the inspiration of the Holy Spirit. For holy mother Church, relying on the belief of the Apostles (see John 20:31; 2 Tim. 3:16; 2 Peter 1:19-20, 3:15-16), holds that the books of both the Old and New Testaments in their entirety, with all their parts, are sacred and canonical because written under the inspiration of the Holy Spirit, they have God as their author and have been handed on as such to the Church herself. In composing the sacred books, God chose men and while employed by Him they made use of their powers and abilities, so that with Him acting in them and through them, they, as true authors, consigned to writing everything and only those things which He wanted.

Therefore, since everything asserted by the inspired authors or sacred writers must be held to be asserted by the Holy Spirit, it follows that the books of Scripture must be acknowledged as teaching solidly, faithfully and without error that truth which God wanted put into sacred writings for the sake of salvation. Therefore "all Scripture is divinely inspired and has its use for teaching the truth and refuting error, for reformation of manners and discipline in right living, so that the man who belongs to God may be efficient and equipped for good work of every kind" (2 Tim. 3:16-17, Greek text).

12. However, since God speaks in Sacred Scripture through men in human fashion, the interpreter of Sacred Scripture, in order to see clearly what God wanted to communicate to us, should carefully investigate what meaning the sacred writers really intended, and what God wanted to manifest by means of their words.

To search out the intention of the sacred writers, attention should be given, among other things, to "literary forms." For truth is set forth and expressed differently in texts which are variously historical, prophetic, poetic, or of other forms of discourse. The interpreter must investigate what meaning the sacred writer intended to express and actually expressed in particular circumstances by using contemporary literary forms in accordance with the situation of his own time and culture. For the correct understanding of what the sacred author wanted to assert, due attention must be paid to the customary and characteristic styles of feeling, speaking and narrating which prevailed at the time of the sacred writer, and to the patterns men normally employed at that period in their everyday dealings with one another.

But, since Holy Scripture must be read and interpreted in the sacred spirit in which it was written, no less serious attention must be given to the content and unity of the whole of Scripture if the meaning of the sacred texts is to be correctly worked out. The living tradition of the whole Church must be taken into account along with the harmony which exists between elements of the faith. It is the task of exegetes to work according to these rules toward a better understanding and explanation of the meaning of Sacred Scripture, so that through preparatory study the judgment of the Church may mature. For all of what has been said about the way of interpreting Scripture is subject finally to the judgment of the Church, which carries out the divine commission and ministry of guarding and interpreting the word of God.

13. In Sacred Scripture, therefore, while the truth and holiness of God always remains intact, the marvelous "condescension" of eternal wisdom is clearly shown, "that we may learn the gentle kindness of God, which words cannot express, and how far He has gone in adapting His language with thoughtful concern for our weak human nature." For the words of God, expressed in human language, have been made like human discourse, just as the word of the eternal Father, when He took to Himself the flesh of human weakness, was in every way made like men.

1. Under whose inspiration is Scripture written? _____

2. Because of the one who inspired the Scriptures, what can be said about them?

   _____

   _____

3. What does 2 Timothy 3:16-17 say about Scripture? _____

   _____

4. Since God used human authors, what two things need to be taken into consideration when reading Scripture?

   _____

   _____

5. According to the reading, we must pay attention to the different "literary forms" in Scripture. What is meant by this, and why is this important?

   _____

   _____

6. What do the Scriptures ultimately teach us about God and how He relates to us?

   _____

   _____

Catechism Focus Questions

Directions: Read *Catechism of the Catholic Church* nos. 109-118, then answer the questions below.

1. In one or two sentences, summarize the main point(s) of paragraphs 109-111.

   _____

   _____

2. Paragraphs 112-114 give three criteria for reading Scripture. What are those three criteria? Briefly explain each in your own words.

   _____

   _____

   _____

3. What are the two senses of Scripture?

   _____

   _____

4. What sense are the allegorical, moral, and anagogical senses parts of?

   _____

   _____

   _____

5. Briefly define what is meant by the allegorical, moral, and anagogical senses.

   _____

   _____

   _____

What Sense Is It Anyway?

Directions: Read each of the following examples. After each example, determine whether it is referring to the **literal** sense or one of the three spiritual senses (**allegorical**, **moral**, **anagogical**).

_____ 1. Abraham almost sacrificing his beloved son, Isaac, points to God the Father sacrificing His beloved Son, Jesus.

_____ 2. Jesus washing the feet of the Apostles teaches us that we are called to serve others.

_____ 3. Abram obeys God and moves from the land of Ur.

_____ 4. The city of Jerusalem and the Temple are merely symbols of the Heavenly Kingdom that awaits us.

_____ 5. The book of Revelation tells of St. John's vision of the great wedding feast of the Lamb, partially fulfilled in the Mass but ultimately pointing to our heavenly destiny.

_____ 6. The Beatitudes give us a framework of what it means to be a disciple of Jesus.

_____ 7. In the story of Noah and the Flood, the Flood foreshadows Baptism, and the Ark, as a means of salvation for Noah and his family, foreshadows the Church as a means of salvation for us.

_____ 8. Jesus wept for His friend Lazarus, who had died.

_____ 9. Moses delivering God's people from slavery foreshadows Jesus delivering us from sin.

_____ 10. The faith of Abraham gives us an example of the kind of faith and trust we are called to have.

Writing Styles of the Bible

Catechism of the Catholic Church

109 In Sacred Scripture, God speaks to man in a human way. To interpret Scripture correctly, the reader must be attentive to what the human authors truly wanted to affirm, and to what God wanted to reveal to us by their words.

110 In order to discover *the sacred authors' intention*, the reader must take into account the conditions of their time and culture, the literary genres in use at that time, and the modes of feeling, speaking and narrating then current. "For the fact is that truth is differently presented and expressed in the various types of historical writing, in prophetical and poetical texts, and in other forms of literary expression."

Writing Styles

Narrative Narratives tell a story in a straightforward way, recounting some event or story of an important person in Israel's history.

Law The Law, mostly contained in the first five books of the Bible, called the Pentateuch, are writings that communicate how best to love God and each other. The Law is necessary to free us from sin and direct us toward the ultimate goodness that is God.

Prophecy The prophetic writings of the Bible foretold the consequences of the current course of action of the people of Israel and called them to repentance and right worship of God. Prophetic writings also warn us today of similar actions and consequences in our own lives and call us to turn away from sin and pursue holiness. These writings would also tell of the fulfillment of God's promises to His people and of His loving care for them.

Poetry The poetic writings of the Bible use metaphorical and artistic language to communicate basic truths about God and human nature. Although they typically do not rhyme, they follow a certain rhythm and meter and employ characteristic literary devices such as parallelism and repetition.

Wisdom/proverbs   Wisdom literature comments on the human condition using wise quotable sayings. These often offer advice for a wide range of topics and situations.

Parable   Parables are short stories that communicate layers of truth. Jesus often used parables to teach His disciples.

Genealogy   Genealogies record family ancestries and reveal important family connections between individuals in the Bible.

Epistle/letter   The epistles are letters written by St. Paul and the other Apostles to early Christian communities and individuals to encourage them in their faith. They offer advice and teaching to their recipients that often apply to our situations today.

Apocalyptic   Apocalyptic writings communicate truths about God and our salvation through visions, strange imagery, and symbolism.

Look up the following passages together with your teacher and discuss why they are examples of the given writing style of the Bible.

1. **Narrative:** Genesis 12:1-4 _____

2. **Law:** Exodus 20:1-17 _____

3. **Prophecy:** Jonah 3:4-5 _____

4. **Poetry:** Psalm 78:1-4 _____

5. **Wisdom/proverbs:** Proverbs 19:1 _____

6. **Parable:** Mark 4:3-9 _____

7. **Genealogy:** Matthew 1:1-17 _____

8. **Epistle/letter:** Philippians 1:1-2 _____

9. **Apocalyptic:** Revelation 12:1-18 _____

Group Bible Verse Scavenger Hunt

Directions: As a group, find an example of each of the following literary styles in your Bible. Write down the book, chapter(s), and verses for each. Each example should be at least four verses long. You may not use any of the examples from the previous activity. The first group to finish correctly will receive a prize.

1. Narrative: _____

2. Law: _____

3. Prophecy: _____

4. Poetry: _____

5. Wisdom/proverbs: _____

6. Parable: _____
   (Bonus point if you can find one in the Old Testament!)

7. Genealogy: _____

8. Epistle/letter: _____

9. Apocalyptic: _____

Individual Bible Verse Scavenger Hunt

Directions: Find an example of each of the following literary styles in your Bible. Write down the book, chapter(s), and verses for each. Each example should be at least four verses long. You may not use any of the examples from the previous activity that you used to complete the group scavenger hunt. The first three people to finish correctly will receive a prize.

1. Narrative: _____

2. Law: _____

3. Prophecy: _____

4. Poetry: _____

5. Wisdom/proverbs: _____

6. Parable: _____

    (Bonus point if you can find one in the Old Testament!)

7. Genealogy: _____

8. Epistle/letter: _____

9. Apocalyptic: _____

An Introduction to the Bible Note-Taking Aid

Directions: Fill in the blanks as your teacher goes over the information on the PowerPoint.

What Is Sacred Scripture?

1. Scripture is the _____ written down and
    _____ to us throughout history.

2. Sacred Scripture is _____.

3. "In the sacred books, the _____ who is in
    _____ comes _____ to meet his
    _____ and _____ with them" (CCC 104).

Salvation History

4. The Scriptures comprise the story of our _____ known as
    _____.

5. Define **Salvation History:** The history of _____ coming to
    _____ in time through the _____ of His
    _____ and _____ so that we might be
    _____ from _____ - _____
    _____ from Him.

A Living Word

6. The Scriptures are a _____. We must ask God to open our minds to
    understand the Scriptures and apply them to our own lives.

7. Scripture is the word of God _____ in _____ words.

8. St. _____ says, "Ignorance of _____ is
    ignorance of _____.

When Was the Bible Written?

9. Written between _____.

10. Old Testament: Parts during _____, the bulk of it was written

    _____.

11. New Testament: _____.

By Whom Was the Bible Written?

12. The Old Testament was written by _____.

13. The New Testament was written by _____.

The authors lived in the Holy Land and also in other parts of the world, such as Greece and Egypt.

How Did the Canon Come to Be?

14. The Church, under the guidance of the _____ has

    the _____ to determine which books belong in the

    _____ of Scripture.

15. Define **Canon of Scripture:** _____.

16. AD 393 – Council of _____ : List of books for the Canon issued.

17. AD 3397 – Council of _____ : Same list given again.

18. AD 1546 – Council of _____: Makes a definite decree that the Canon
    as we know it today is the list of books inspired by God.

Division of Books in the Old Testament

19. _____Books

20. _____Books

21. _____Books

22. _____Books

Old and New Testaments

23. Define **Testament:**

   _____

   _____

24. The Old Testament is _____ in the _____ and

   the _____ is _____ in the _____

   _____.

25. The Old Testament is the story of _____.

26. It needs to be read in the light of _____.

27. The Old Testament has its _____ as well and a lot can be learned

   from it _____.

28. The New Testament focuses _____,

29. The _____ are the _____ we have for the life of

   _____.

30. The Old Testament and the New Testament are a collection of several

   _____ that make up _____ story!

Connecting the Old and New Testaments

Directions: Read the following passage from Scripture and then complete the questions that follow.

Matthew 1:1-17
The Genealogy of Jesus

The book of the genealogy of Jesus Christ, the son of David, the son of Abraham. Abraham became the father of Isaac, Isaac the father of Jacob, Jacob the father of Judah and his brothers. Judah became the father of Perez and Zerah, whose mother was Tamar. Perez became the father of Hezron, Hezron the father of Ram, Ram the father of Amminadab. Amminadab became the father of Nahshon, Nahshon the father of Salmon, Salmon the father of Boaz, whose mother was Rahab. Boaz became the father of Obed, whose mother was Ruth. Obed became the father of Jesse, Jesse the father of David the king. David became the father of Solomon, whose mother had been the wife of Uriah. Solomon became the father of Rehoboam, Rehoboam the father of Abijah, Abijah the father of Asaph. Asaph became the father of Jehoshaphat, Jehoshaphat the father of Joram, Joram the father of Uzziah. Uzziah became the father of Jotham, Jotham the father of Ahaz, Ahaz the father of Hezekiah. Hezekiah became the father of Manasseh, Manasseh the father of Amos, Amos the father of Josiah. Josiah became the father of Jechoniah and his brothers at the time of the Babylonian exile. After the Babylonian exile, Jechoniah became the father of Shealtiel, Shealtiel the father of Zerubbabel, Zerubbabel the father of Abiud. Abiud became the father of Eliakim, Eliakim the father of Azor, Azor the father of Zadok. Zadok became the father of Achim, Achim the father of Eliud, Eliud the father of Eleazar. Eleazar became the father of Matthan, Matthan the father of Jacob, Jacob the father of Joseph, the husband of Mary. Of her was born Jesus who is called the Messiah. Thus the total number of generations from Abraham to David is fourteen generations; from David to the Babylonian exile, fourteen generations; from the Babylonian exile to the Messiah, fourteen generations.

1. Aside from a list of names, what does this genealogy show?

   _____

2. Why do you think Matthew chose to include this genealogy in his Gospel? What point do you think he was trying to make?

   _____

3. Which names here do you recognize from the Old Testament? How does this help you see and understand the connection between them and Jesus a little more?

_____

_____

_____

4. Based on what you know about the Old Testament and this genealogy, try to place the following events in chronological order. Number each event in order, 1-16.

☐ A. David becomes king, and God makes a covenant with David, promising his son an everlasting throne.

☐ B. God asks Abraham to sacrifice Isaac but spares him in the end.

☐ C. The Holy Spirit descends on the Apostles, and they begin their mission of spreading the Gospel to the ends of the earth.

☐ D. God creates Adam and Eve, places them in the Garden of Eden and tells them not to eat from the Tree of Knowledge of Good and Evil.

☐ E. Moses leads the people out of slavery in Egypt.

☐ F. God spares Noah and his family from the flood by having him build an ark.

☐ G. The angel Gabriel appears to Mary and tells her she will be the Mother of Jesus.

☐ H. God calls Abraham to move and tells him he will have descendants as numerous as the stars.

☐ I. Solomon becomes King and builds the first temple.

☐ J. Adam and Eve commit the first sin and bring about the Fall.

☐ K. Jesus suffers, dies, and rises from the dead.

☐   L.   Moses gives the Israelites the Ten Commandments.

☐   M.   Jesus ascends into Heaven.

☐   N.   Christ is born.

☐   O.   After Adam and Eve sin, God promises them He will send a Savior.

☐   P.   Joshua leads the Israelites into the Promised Land after 40 years in the desert.

5.   How does seeing the Old and New Testaments as one story provide a clearer understanding of the Bible and aid in your own spiritual life?

_____

_____

_____

_____

_____

Heroes of the Bible

Directions: Choose your favorite figure from the Old Testament and write two well-constructed five- to seven-sentence paragraphs in the space provided that reflect on how and why you see the figure as a "hero" even though he or she wasn't perfect. How in some way does this person help point you to Jesus?

_____

_____

_____

_____

_____

_____

_____

_____

_____

_____

_____

_____

_____

_____

_____

_____

_____

Salvation History Collection

Salvation History through Art
Discussion Questions

Directions: Look at the Salvation History collection of art, then discuss with your group the questions below.

Conversation Questions

1. Of all the images, which is your favorite? Why?

2. What stood out to you about your favorite image?

3. What one thing stands out to you in each image?

4. How does seeing each of these images help you understand or contemplate the story of our salvation more clearly?

Understanding Covenants

Directions: Read the information below, then use it to complete the chart on pages 92-93.

In order to understand the Bible more clearly we must understand what a covenant is. Covenant is the central theme throughout Scripture. It comes from the Latin word *convenire*, which means "to come together" or "to agree." A covenant can be defined as a formal and solemn pact or agreement binding two or more parties to mutual responsibilities; an exchange of persons. A covenant is all about forging *relationships* and *family bonds*.

A covenant can sound a lot like a contract. However there are a few key differences between a contract and a covenant that are important to understand:

Contract	Covenant
Exchange of goods and services.	Exchange of persons.
Sets up obligations, but they are not personal obligations.	Personal responsibilities flow from a covenant. These responsibilities are based on our personal relationship and commitment to the other person.
Based merely on human words and promises.	Based on God's word.
Relationships may end if terms are broken.	Relationships endure even if covenant terms are not kept.
50/50 relationships.	Not 50/50 relationships, but 100/100.

The point is that covenants are all about a mutual exchange of love between two parties. Covenants are the way God chose to relate to us. Covenant is who God is.

God makes six major covenants throughout Scripture:

> - The Covenant with Adam.
> - The Covenant with Noah.
> - The Covenant with Abraham.
> - The Covenant with Moses.
> - The Covenant with David.
> - The New Covenant in Christ.

Each covenant contains a mediator, a promise, and a sign.

These, however, are not the only covenants made. They are the major ones, but smaller covenants are made several times throughout Scripture. A covenant is made by swearing an oath, invoking blessings and curses on the person (curses if the covenant is not kept), and saying or performing ritual words and actions. Whenever you see one of these things taking place in the Bible, a covenant is being forged, even if the word *covenant* is not specifically used.

A common misconception people have is that a covenant is simply an agreement or promise between God and man. However, covenants can take place between people as well. For example, we call marriage a covenant.

Understanding what a covenant is and how covenants work is essential to our understanding of the Bible. It helps us draw the connection between the Old and New Testaments more clearly and helps us more clearly come to know our Father in Heaven and how He pours out His love and graces on us.

Major Covenants throughout Scripture

Directions: Every covenant has a promise, a mediator, and a sign. Each covenant also signifies a progression or growth in God's family. Using the information in **Understanding Covenants**, fill in the following chart by placing the squares you receive from your teacher in the appropriate space.

Covenant Mediator	Covenant Promise	Covenant Sign	Covenant Progression
Adam			
Noah			
Abraham			

Covenant Mediator	Covenant Promise	Covenant Sign	Covenant Progression
Moses			
David			
Jesus			

Icon of the Transfiguration
BY ANONYMOUS (12TH CENTURY)

Saint Catherine's Monastery, Sinai (Egypt).

Applying Typology

Directions: A *type* in Scripture is a person or thing in the Old Testament that foreshadows a person or thing in the New Testament. Isaac is a type of Jesus Christ, and the Passover is a type of the Eucharist and the Crucifixion. Complete the charts below by matching the strips provided by your teacher to show how Christ fulfills each of these events.

Sacrifice of Isaac	Sacrifice of Christ

Sacrifice of Isaac	Sacrifice of Christ

The Passover	The Eucharist/Crucifixion

The Passover	The Eucharist/Crucifixion

Psalm 139

Directions: Read the Psalm, then answer the reflection questions that follow.

LORD, you have probed me, you know me: you know when I sit and stand; you understand my thoughts from afar. You sift through my travels and my rest; with all my ways you are familiar. Even before a word is on my tongue, LORD, you know it all. Behind and before you encircle me and rest your hand upon me. Such knowledge is too wonderful for me, far too lofty for me to reach. Where can I go from your spirit? From your presence, where can I flee? If I ascend to the heavens, you are there; if I lie down in Sheol, there you are. If I take the wings of dawn and dwell beyond the sea, even there your hand guides me, your right hand holds me fast. If I say, "Surely darkness shall hide me, and night shall be my light"–Darkness is not dark for you, and night shines as the day. Darkness and light are but one.

You formed my inmost being; you knit me in my mother's womb. I praise you, because I am wonderfully made; wonderful are your works! My very self you know. My bones are not hidden from you, when I was being made in secret, fashioned in the depths of the earth. Your eyes saw me unformed; in your book all are written down; my days were shaped, before one came to be.

How precious to me are your designs, O God; how vast the sum of them! Were I to count them, they would outnumber the sands; when I complete them, still you are with me. When you would destroy the wicked, O God, the bloodthirsty depart from me! Your foes who conspire a plot against you are exalted in vain.

Do I not hate, LORD, those who hate you? Those who rise against you, do I not loathe? With fierce hatred I hate them, enemies I count as my own. Probe me, God, know my heart; try me, know my thoughts. See if there is a wicked path in me; lead me along an ancient path.

1. How does the psalmist describe the way God knows us? How does it make you feel to understand that God knows you in this way? Does this change the way you might think of Him and pray to Him?

   _____

   _____

2. Do you ever feel lonely or misunderstood? The psalmist tells us that God has known us even before we were born and that He knows our very self. How might this change our feelings of loneliness or of not being understood?

   _____

   _____

3. Describe a time when you were amazed by God's creation around you. How do you show your love for God's creation?

    _____

    _____

    _____

4. How can you defend God to others who might not know Him or love Him?

    _____

    _____

    _____

My Timeline

Directions: Think about important events in your life thus far and document them in the timeline boxes. Then, using the key below, write next to each box how you know this occurred in your life.

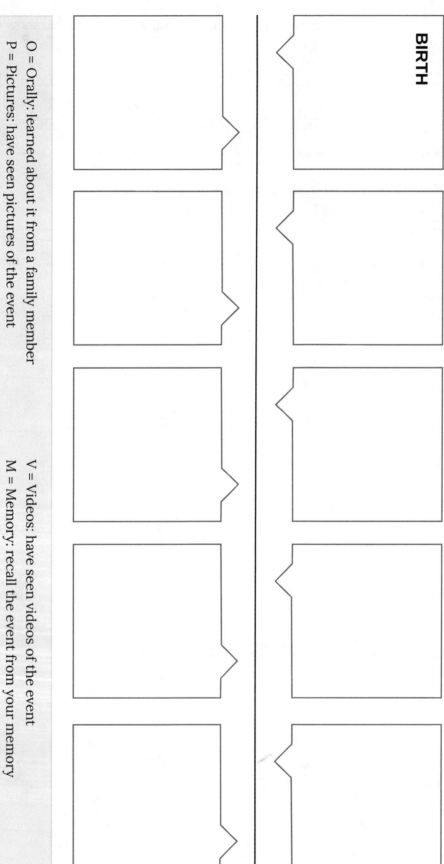

BIRTH

O = Orally: learned about it from a family member
P = Pictures: have seen pictures of the event
V = Videos: have seen videos of the event
M = Memory: recall the event from your memory

Stages of Gospel Formation
Note-Taking Guide

Directions: The four Gospels have a central place in the Bible because Christ Jesus is their center. Answer the questions and fill in the blanks as you learn about the stages of the formation of the Gospels and the development of the New Testament.

Organization of the New Testament

1. Number of books in New Testament: _____

2. Classified in same order as _____,

    A. _____ ⟶ 4 Gospels – teach New Law

    C. _____ ⟶ Acts of the Apostles; early Church history

    D. _____ ⟶ Epistles; tell how to live as Christians

    E. _____ ⟶ Revelation – symbols and images as reminder of the Old Testament

The Four Gospels

3. The Gospels are _____ of Scripture because in them we meet

    _____.

4. _____ means "Good News" of God's _____ and

    love revealed in the _____, Death, and Resurrection of Christ.

5. _____ means "one who is sent" / "messenger."

6. _____ is one of the four authors to whom is ascribed the writing of the

    Gospels.

7. The Synoptic Gospels are Matthew, Mark, and Luke – _____ means to

    see from similar view points

8. Gospel of John – focus on _____.

Development of Gospels: 3 stages

9. Jesus' earthly _____ and _____.

10. Apostolic _____.

11. Writing the _____.

Symbols of Evangelists

12. Matthew: _____

13. Mark: _____

14. Luke : _____

15. John: _____

Matthew

16. Year: AD _____

17. Who was Matthew? _____

18. Audience: _____

19. Focus: _____

20. Answers two questions:

_____

_____

Mark

21. Year: AD _____

22. Who was Mark? _____

23. Audience: _____

24. Focus: _____

25. Presents Jesus as:

_____

_____

Luke

26. Year: AD _____

27. Who was Luke? _____

28. Audience: _____

29. Focus: _____

30. What is unique about the sources of Luke's Gospel?

_____

_____

John

31. Year: AD _____

32. Who was John? _____

33. Audience: _____

34. Focus: _____

35. Two purposes of John's Gospel:

_____

_____

New Testament Quiz

1. List the three stages in the development of the Gospels.

   ➤ _____

   ➤ _____

   ➤ _____

2. Which Gospel writer used Peter as the main source for the story of Christ's life?
   a. Matthew
   b. Mark
   c. Luke
   d. John

3. The evangelist Luke is portrayed as the symbol of the:
   a. Lion
   b. Eagle
   c. Ox
   d. Man

4. The evangelist Mark is portrayed as the symbol of the:
   a. Lion
   b. Eagle
   c. Ox
   d. Man

5. Which evangelist also wrote the Acts of the Apostles?
   a. Matthew
   b. Mark
   c. Luke
   d. John

True or False?

Write true if the statement is true and false if the statement is false.

_____ 6. There are 27 books in the New Testament.

_____ 7. Luke most likely used the Blessed Virgin Mary as his primary source.

_____ 8. John the Apostle was a historian and an eyewitness to many events he described in his writings.

_____ 9. The Synoptic Gospels tell the story of Jesus' life very differently from one another.

Interview Questions

Directions: Take turns interviewing a partner using the following questions. Record your partner's answers. Then think about your own answers to the interview questions and write a five- to seven-sentence paragraph that answers the reflection question.

1. Where were you born? _____

2. If you were born someplace other than here, when did you move here? Why?

   _____

   _____

3. What is your favorite color? _____

4. What is your favorite food? _____

5. What is your favorite subject in school? Why?

   _____

   _____

6. What is your favorite thing to do with your mom? _____

7. What is your favorite thing to do with your dad? _____

8. What are two things you are really good at? _____

9. What are two things you are not so good at? _____

10. What do you want to be when you grow up? _____

Reflection Question

Think about your answers to the interview questions. On your own paper, answer the following questions: How do our experiences, preferences, and even the places we live in and the people around us help to shape the person we are today? How have your experiences, your preferences, the places you've lived, and the people in your life helped to shape you into the person you are today?

World of the New Testament Notes

Directions: Answer the questions and fill in the blanks as you learn about the world of the New Testament.

Maccabean Revolt

1. Greek King _____ forced the Jews to _____
   and _____.

2. In 164 BC the Maccabean rebellion defeated the _____and won
   back _____.

3. The Temple of Jerusalem was rededicated to _____.

4. _____ is a celebration of the purification of the Temple.

Hasmonean Dynasty

5. The Maccabean army eventually reconquered nearly all of _____.

6. A new dynasty was established under the rule of _____.

7. The Hasmonean kingdom ruled as an independent _____until
   63 BC when the _____ took over.

Had the prophecies been fulfilled?

8. _____was restored.

9. There was a _____.

10. There was a _____. So what was the problem?

11. The promises and prophesies were about a king from the tribe of
    _____, a Son of _____.

12. The _____were not in the line of _____.

Two Powerful Groups

13. The Pharisees: In order for Israel to remain faithful to God, the people must

    _____ and hold strictly to _____.

14. Non-Jews were also known as _____.

15. The Pharisees believed in the _____ and

    _____, as did Jesus!

16. The Sadducees: Wealthy _____ and _____ who

    believed the only way for Judaism to survive was to cooperate with _____.

17. The Pentateuch is the _____.

18. The Sadducees believe only the Pentateuch was _____.

19. The Sadducees did not believe in the _____,

    _____, angels, or _____.

Herod the Great

20. King of _____ at the time of Jesus' birth.

21. Called "the Great" because of the prosperous _____and

    _____, not because of his holiness.

22. He cooperated with the Romans who allowed him to rule as long as he

    _____.

23. Not a Jew, but deceived the people into thinking he was a descendant of _____

    and called himself "_____, King of the Jews."

24. After his death, the kingdom split into _____.

The Fullness of Time

25. _____ – The political state of the world was stable.

26. _____ was the easiest it had ever been. Using the

    _____, one could travel from one end of the empire to the

    other safely.

27. Same _____.

28. Same _____.

29. Rome's religion had become irrelevant to the people, so _____
    faith was spreading more.

Galilee

30. Jesus lived in the northern town of _____ in Galilee.

31. People from Galilee had the reputation of being _____,

    uneducated, and _____.

32. Fertile soil and because of its closeness to _____, there were

    many _____.

The Samaritans

33. Ethnically mixed population in _____ who were considered

    _____ by the rest of Jewish society.

34. Worshiped the one true _____, but differently than _____.

35. Jews were _____ by law from associating with Samaritans.

Geography of the Bible

Directions: Fill in the blanks with the correct term from the box. Then, answer the reflection question.

Egypt	Middle	Galilee
of the Nations	Jerusalem	Fertile Crescent	Megido

1. The _____ links two rivers at each end: the Nile and Euphrates.

2. Mesopotamia means "_____ of the rivers."

3. _____ and Assyria / Babylon were the two most powerful territory regions.

4. The Promised Land was the crossroads of the world, specifically called _____ or in Hebrew, Harmagedon.

5. The Northern part of Israel was called _____.

6. The isolated, very Jewish part located in the hills was _____.

Reflection Question

Why did God purposefully place His people in this area? How does this help us understand Jesus' ministry to God's people?

_____

_____

_____

_____

_____

The Pharisees, Sadducees, and Scribes Comic Strip

Directions: Read the selected stories of Jesus' encounters with the Pharisees, Sadducees, and scribes. Choose one of the Scripture stories to illustrate as a comic strip using the frames.

Jesus' Encounters

1. Mark 12:13-17

2. Matthew 22:34-40

3. Luke 6:6-11

4. Mark 2:23-28

My Comic Strip

Scripture Passage: _____

World of the New Testament Crossword Puzzle

Directions: Using your notes, complete the crossword puzzle.

Down:

1. This influential group believed in the afterlife and resurrection of the body.

2. This revolt by the Jews won back Jerusalem and the Temple from Greek rule.

4. Non-Jewish people.

7. Region of Judea Jesus lived in.

8. He was king of Judea when Jesus was born.

9. The stable political condition of the world during the Roman Empire.

Across:

3. The Hasmonean kings were not descendants of this Hebrew king.

5. Jewish holiday that celebrates the purification of the Temple.

6. This influential group believed only the first five books of Scripture were canonical.

10. This dynasty re-conquered nearly all of David's old kingdom.

11. Greek king who forced the Jews to worship gods.

12. An ethnically mixed population in Israel.

13. The first five books of the Bible.

Four Reasons for the Incarnation Note-Taking Guide

Directions: Read about the four reasons for the Incarnation from the *Catechism of the Catholic Church* nos. 456-460, then fill in the blanks with the correct information.

Why Did the Word Become Flesh?

456 With the Nicene Creed, we answer by confessing: "For us men and for our

(1.)_____ he came down from (2.)_____; by the

power of the Holy Spirit, he became incarnate of the Virgin Mary, and was made man."

457 The Word became flesh for us *in* (3.)_____ *to save us by reconciling*

us with God, who "loved us and sent his Son to be the expiation for our sins": "the Father

has sent his Son as the Savior of the world," and "he was revealed to take away sins":

Sick, our nature demanded to be healed; fallen, to be raised up; dead, to rise again. We had

lost the possession of the (4.)_____; it was necessary for it to be

given back to us. Closed in the darkness, it was necessary to bring us the light;

(5.)_____, we awaited a Savior; prisoners, help; slaves, a liberator.

Are these things minor or insignificant? Did they not move God to descend to

(6.)_____ nature and visit it, since humanity was in so miserable

and unhappy a state?

458 The Word became flesh *so that thus we might know God's love*: "In this the love of God was

made manifest (7.)_____us, that God sent his only Son into the

world, so that we might live through him." "For God so loved the world that he gave his

only Son, that whoever (8.)_____ in him should not perish but have

eternal life."

459 The Word became flesh *to be our model of* (9.)_____: "Take my yoke

upon you, and learn from me." "I am the way, and the truth, and the life; no one comes to

the Father, but by me." On the mountain of the Transfiguration, the Father

(10.)_____: "Listen to him!" Jesus is the model for the Beatitudes and the norm of the new law: "Love one another as I have

(11.)_____ you." This love implies an effective offering of oneself, after his example.

460 The Word became flesh to make us "*partakers of the divine nature*": "For this is why the (12.)

_____ became man, and the Son of God became the Son of man: so that man, by entering into communion with the Word and thus receiving divine sonship, might become a son of God." "For the Son of God became man so that we might

(13.)_____ God." "The only-begotten Son of God, wanting to make us sharers in his divinity, assumed our nature, so that he, made man, might make men gods."

The word *Incarnation* means to become (14.)_____, to take on a

body. The Annunciation was the announcement by the (15.)_____ Gabriel

that through the (16.)_____ of the Holy Spirit, Mary, although a

virgin, was to be the Mother of (17.)_____, the Son of

(18.)_____. Mary does not (19.)_____ why
God has chosen her or how she will bear a son, but despite her fears, she says

(20.)_____ to God's plan. At that moment,

(21.)_____ was conceived in her womb! Mary can be called the

Mother of (22.)_____ since she birthed the person Jesus, who is

God who (23.)_____ man. Jesus had to be fully God and fully man in
order to accomplish our reconciliation.

The Incarnation Quiz

Directions: Without looking in your workbook, and in your own words, define the Incarnation and then write the four reasons for it.

1. What is the Incarnation?

   _____

   _____

   _____

   _____

2. What are the four reasons for the Incarnation?

   ➤ _____

   _____

   ➤ _____

   _____

   ➤ _____

   _____

   ➤ _____

   _____

The Divinity of Jesus

Directions: Read each Scripture passage, then discuss and record what it tells us about the divinity of Jesus.

	Scripture Verse(s)	What does this tell us about the divinity of Jesus?
1	John 1:1-5	
2	John 14:8-10	
3	Matthew 1:23; John 20:24-31	
4	Matthew 16:21; Luke 11:17; John 4:29	

	Scripture Verse(s)	What does this tell us about the divinity of Jesus?
5	Matthew 18:20; 28:20; Acts 18:10	
6	Matthew 8:26–27; 28:18; John 11:38–44; Luke 7:14–15; Revelation 1:8	
7	Matthew 28:18; Revelation 1:5; 19:16	

Reflection Question

Based on what you have read in Scripture about Jesus' divinity, summarize in your own words what it means that Jesus is fully God.

_____

_____

_____

_____

_____

Who Is Jesus?

Directions: Read each statement about Jesus and decide if it is true or false. Then answer the reflection question.

	True or false?	
1. Jesus sometimes got lonely and tired.	True	False
2. Jesus loved everybody.	True	False
3. Jesus had friends He was closer to than others.	True	False
4. Jesus had enemies.	True	False
5. Jesus sometimes felt far from God.	True	False
6. Jesus was courageous and strong.	True	False
7. Jesus sometimes experienced disappointment.	True	False
8. Jesus was tempted to do wrong.	True	False
9. Jesus sinned.	True	False

Reflection Question

Write a well-constructed five- to seven-sentence paragraph that responds to the following prompt:

Which statement and discussion most surprised you? Why? Which statement and discussion do you think people should know about Jesus? Why?

_____

_____

_____

_____

_____

_____

_____

_____

_____

_____

_____

_____

_____

_____

_____

_____

Event in Jesus' Life Interview

Directions: With your partner, read your assigned Scripture story. Then imagine that one of you is a TV reporter who is assigned to cover this event, and the other is a character from the story who saw everything that happened. (In the first story, it could be an angel or a shepherd. In the second, it could be Mary, Joseph, or Simeon.) The reporter should determine the important information that he or she would want to make sure appeared in the interview and some follow-up questions to ask. The character from the story, then, should act in character and answer the reporter's questions. In the space below, write the text of your interview, including the questions asked by the reporter and the character's responses.

Reporter's Questions and Character's Answers

_____

_____

_____

_____

_____

_____

_____

_____

_____

_____

_____

Important Parts of the Story

_____

_____

_____

_____

_____

_____

_____

_____

_____

_____

_____

_____

Scriptural Rosary: The Luminous Mysteries

*The following Scriptural Rosary was taken from the Scriptural Rosary for Justice and Peace found at **USCCB.org**.*

First Luminous Mystery: Baptism in the Jordan

Jesus begins his public ministry being baptized by John.

OUR FATHER...

For our sake he made him to be sin who did not know sin, so that we might become the righteousness of God in him. (2 Cor. 5:21)

HAIL MARY...

He went throughout [the] whole region of the Jordan, proclaiming a baptism of repentance for the forgiveness of sins, as it is written in ... Isaiah:
"A voice of one crying out in the desert:
'Prepare the way of the Lord,
make straight his paths.'" (Luke 3:3)

HAIL MARY...

And the crowds asked him, "What then should we do?" He said to them in reply, "Whoever has two cloaks should share with the person who has none. And whoever has food should do likewise." (Luke 3:10-11)

HAIL MARY...

Jesus also had been baptized ... heaven was opened and the holy Spirit descended upon him in bodily form like a dove. And a voice came from heaven, "You are my beloved Son; with you I am well pleased." (Luke 3:21-22)

HAIL MARY...

Here is my servant whom I uphold,
my chosen one with whom I am pleased.
Upon him I have put my spirit ... (Isa. 42:1)

HAIL MARY...

A bruised reed he shall not break,
and a smoldering wick he shall not quench.
(Isa. 42:3)

HAIL MARY...

I, the LORD, have called you for the victory of justice. (Isa. 42:6)

HAIL MARY...

I formed you, and set you
as a covenant of the people,
a light for the nations. (Isa. 42:6)

HAIL MARY...

The Spirit of the Lord is upon me,
because he has anointed me
to bring glad tidings to the poor. (Luke 4:18)

HAIL MARY...

He has sent me to proclaim liberty to captives
and recovery of sight to the blind,
to let the oppressed go free,
and to proclaim a year acceptable to the Lord.
(Luke 4:18-19)

HAIL MARY...

GLORY BE...

Lord Jesus, help us to persevere in living out our baptismal promises.

Second Luminous Mystery: The Wedding at Cana

Jesus performs his first public sign revealing his true identity, at the request of his mother.

OUR FATHER...

When the wine ran short, the mother of Jesus said to him, "They have no wine." (John 2:3)

HAIL MARY...

Jesus said to her, "Woman, how does your concern affect me? My hour has not yet come." (John 2:4)

HAIL MARY...

His mother said to the servers, "Do whatever he tells you." (John 2:5)

HAIL MARY...

Jesus told them, "Fill the jars with water." So they filled them to the brim. Then he told them, "Draw some out now and take it to the headwaiter." (John 2:7-8)

HAIL MARY...

The headwaiter called the bridegroom and said to him, "Everyone serves good wine first, and then when people have drunk freely, an inferior one; but you have kept the good wine until now." (John 2:9-10)

HAIL MARY...

If I ... have washed your feet, you ought to wash one another's feet. I have given you a model to follow, so that as I have done for you, you should also do. (John 13:14-15)

HAIL MARY...

To you who hear I say, love your enemies, do good to those who hate you, bless those who curse you, pray for those who mistreat you. (Luke 6:27-28)

HAIL MARY...

Stop judging and you will not be judged. Stop condemning and you will not be condemned. Forgive and you will be forgiven. (Luke 6:37)

HAIL MARY...

Then he said to all, "If anyone wishes to come after me, he must deny himself and take up his cross daily and follow me." (Luke 9:23)

HAIL MARY...

This is my commandment: love one another as I love you. (John 15:12)

HAIL MARY...

GLORY BE...

Lord Jesus, open us to the power of your grace to change our hearts and lives.

Third Luminous Mystery: Proclamation of the Kingdom of God

After John was arrested, Jesus began proclaiming the Good News of God's kingdom.

OUR FATHER...

Jesus came to Galilee proclaiming the gospel of God. (Mark 1:14)

HAIL MARY...

This is the time of fulfillment. The kingdom of God is at hand. Repent, and believe in the gospel. (Mark 1:15)

HAIL MARY...

The Spirit of the Lord is upon me,
because he has anointed me
to bring glad tidings to the poor. (Luke 4:18)

HAIL MARY...

He has sent me to proclaim liberty to captives
and recovery of sight to the blind,
to let the oppressed go free,
and to proclaim a year acceptable to the Lord.
(Luke 4:18-19)

HAIL MARY...

Today this scripture passage is fulfilled in your hearing. (Luke 4:21)

HAIL MARY...

You have heard that it was said, "An eye for an eye and a tooth for a tooth." But I say to you ... when someone strikes you on [your] right cheek, turn the other one to him as well." (Matthew 5:38-39)

HAIL MARY...

You have heard that it was said, "You shall love your neighbor and hate your enemy." But I say to you, love your enemies, and pray for those who persecute you. (Matthew 5:43-44)

HAIL MARY...

Do not store up for yourselves treasures on earth. ...But store up treasures in heaven ... for where your treasure is, there also will your heart be. (Matthew 6:19-21)

HAIL MARY...

Do to others whatever you would have them do to you. This is the law and the prophets. (Matthew 7:12)

HAIL MARY...

Without cost you have received; without cost you are to give. (Matthew 10:8)

HAIL MARY...

GLORY BE...

Lord Jesus, fill us with the desire to strive for ongoing conversion.

Fourth Luminous Mystery: The Transfiguration

Jesus is seen with Moses and Elijah, confirming that his suffering will end in glory.

OUR FATHER...

Jesus took Peter, James, and John his brother, and led them up a high mountain by themselves. And he was transfigured before them; his face shone like the sun and his clothes became white as light. (Matthew 17:1-2)

HAIL MARY...

Two men were conversing with him, Moses and Elijah, who appeared in glory and spoke of his exodus that he was going to accomplish in Jerusalem. (Luke 9:30-31)

HAIL MARY...

Peter and his companions ... saw his glory and the two men standing with him. (Luke 9:32)

HAIL MARY...

Peter said..."Master, it is good that we are here; let us make three tents..." But he did not know what he was saying. (Luke 9:33)

HAIL MARY...

A voice [said], "This is my beloved Son, with whom I am well pleased; listen to him." (Matthew 17:5)

HAIL MARY...

But Jesus came and touched them, saying, "Rise, and do not be afraid." And when the disciples raised their eyes, they saw no one else but Jesus alone. (Matthew 17:7-8)

HAIL MARY...

Through him was life, and this life was the light of the human race; the light shines in the darkness, and the darkness has not overcome it. (John 1:4-5)

HAIL MARY...

No one has ever seen God. The only Son, God, who is at the Father's side, has revealed him. (John 1:18)

HAIL MARY...

All of us, gazing with unveiled face on the glory of the Lord, are being transformed into the same image from glory to glory, as from the Lord who is the Spirit. (2 Corinthians 3:18)

HAIL MARY...

You are the light of the world. ...[Y]our light must shine before others, that they may see your good deeds and glorify your heavenly Father. (Matthew 5:14, 16)

HAIL MARY...

GLORY BE...

Lord Jesus, grant us the courage to shine your light in our lives.

Fifth Luminous Mystery: Institution of the Eucharist

At the last supper, Jesus instructs us to remember him in celebration of the Eucharist.

OUR FATHER...

Before the feast of Passover, Jesus knew that his hour had come to pass from this world to the Father. He loved his own in the world and he loved them to the end. (John 13:1)

HAIL MARY...

My appointed time draws near; in your house I shall celebrate the Passover with my disciples. (Matthew 26:18)

HAIL MARY...

I have eagerly desired to eat this Passover with you before I suffer, for, I tell you, I shall not eat it [again] until there is fulfillment in the kingdom of God. (Luke 22:15-16)

HAIL MARY...

Then he took the bread, said the blessing, broke it, and gave it to them, saying, "This is my body, which will be given for you; do this in memory of me." (Luke 22:19)

HAIL MARY...

And likewise the cup after they had eaten, saying, "This cup is the new covenant in my blood, which will be shed for you." (Luke 22:20)

HAIL MARY...

For as often as you eat this bread and drink the cup, you proclaim the death of the Lord until he comes. (1 Corinthians 11:26)

HAIL MARY...

I pray not only for them, but also for those who will believe in me through their word, so that they may all be one ... that the world may believe that you sent me. (John 17:20-21)

HAIL MARY...

Now you are Christ's body, and individually parts of it. (1 Corinthians 12:27)

HAIL MARY...

For in one Spirit we were all baptized into one body, whether Jews or Greeks, slaves or free persons, and we were all given to drink of one Spirit. (1 Corinthians 12:13)

HAIL MARY...

If [one] part suffers, all the parts suffer with it; if one part is honored, all the parts share its joy. (1 Corinthians 12:26)

HAIL MARY...

GLORY BE...

Lord Jesus, make of us a sign of the unity for which you prayed.

The Hail Holy Queen (The Salve Regina)

Hail, holy Queen, mother of mercy,
our life, our sweetness, and our hope.
To you we cry, poor banished children of Eve;
to you we send up our sighs,
mourning and weeping in this valley of tears.

Turn, then, most gracious advocate,
your eyes of mercy toward us;

and after this, our exile,
show unto us the blessed fruit of your womb, Jesus.

O clement, O loving, O sweet Virgin Mary.

Amen.

Christ on the Cross
BY LEON BONNAT (C. 1874)

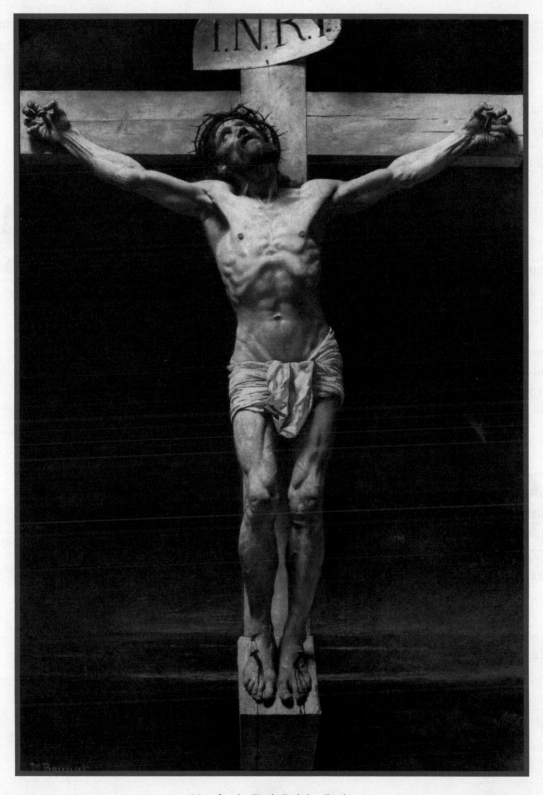

Musée du Petit Palais, Paris.

The Crucifixion of Jesus

Directions: Read the story of the Crucifixion of Jesus from John 19 and then fill in the chart with as much detail as you can about each event, person, place, or statement from the story.

Event	Details about the event
The Scourging	
Pilate	
Pilate and Jesus' Conversation	
The Jews, Chief Priests, and the Crowd	
Caesar	
Golgotha	

Event	Details about the event
The Inscription on the Cross	
Jesus' Clothes	
Those Present at the Foot of the Cross	
Jesus' Mother	
"I Thirst."	
Jesus' Death	
Blood and Water	
The Tomb	

Resurrection Appearances

Directions: Read each Scripture passage about the Resurrection appearances of Christ and summarize each passage in your own words. Then comment briefly on what each passage teaches us about the Resurrection of Christ.

	Scripture Verse(s)	What happens?	What does it teach us about the Resurrection of Christ?
1	John 20:11-18		
2	Luke 24:13-35		
3	Luke 24:36-43		
4	John 21:1-25		
5	Matthew 28:16-20		
6	Luke 24:50-51		

The Calling of St. Matthew
BY CARAVAGGIO (1599–1600)

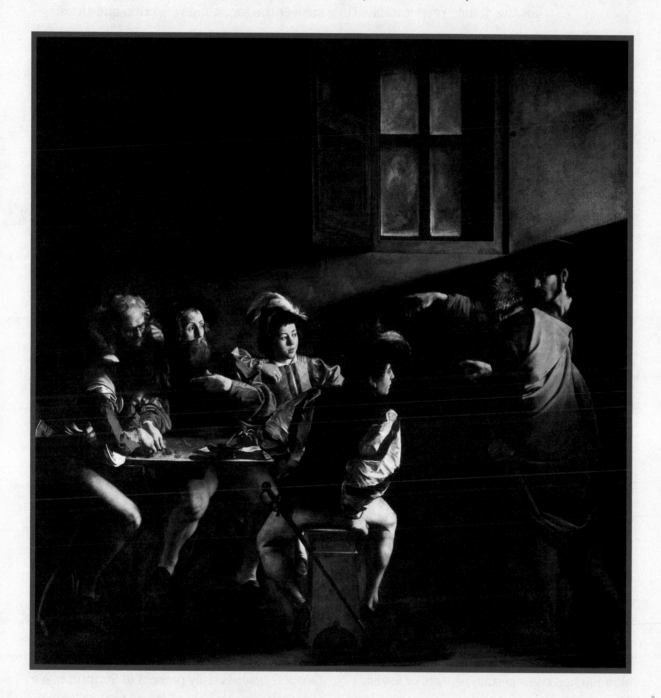

Oil on canvas. San Luigi dei Francesi, Rome.

The Gospel of Matthew

Directions: Read about the intended audience and structure of the Gospel of Matthew and how we should read it today. Then answer the focus and reflection questions.

The Gospels tell the truth about what Jesus really said and really did during His earthly life. Matthew fulfilled the commission Jesus gave the Apostles to teach all He commanded them. Matthew did this by putting in writing, under the inspiration of the Holy Spirit, the Gospel account of Jesus' life and teachings. In other words, Matthew faithfully recorded what Jesus really said and did during His earthly ministry so that it might be preserved for generations to come.

Who is the intended audience of Matthew's Gospel? All four Gospels tell the same story of Jesus Christ's perfect love for us and His sacrifice on the Cross to save us from sin. Even so, they differ in some details. One reason for the differences is that the evangelists were writing for different audiences. St. Matthew wrote primarily for an audience with a Jewish background.

The Jews knew the Old Testament well, so Matthew decided to show his audience how Jesus is the promised Savior and Messiah foretold in the Old Testament. There are more than 100 references to the Old Testament in Matthew's Gospel, more than in any other Gospel. These references include 40 direct quotes and 60 references to other Old Testament texts. Therefore, Matthew assumed his audience knew certain aspects of Jewish life and culture and did not spend a lot of time explaining these things.

Biblical scholars do not always agree on the dating of Matthew's Gospel. Dates vary between AD 50 and 100, although many scholars believe it was written before the destruction of Jerusalem in AD 70.

How is Matthew's Gospel arranged? St. Matthew organized his Gospel very neatly so his reader would be able to remember a lot about Jesus' life and teaching. Matthew's Gospel has 28 chapters and can be divided into seven sections. The first two chapters address Jesus' birth and early childhood. The last three chapters cover His Passion, Death, Resurrection, and Ascension. The middle section, chapters 3 through 25, can be divided into five sections, sometimes called "books." Each of these five sections or "books" follows a pattern of telling of the events of Jesus' life followed by describing Jesus' teaching. Matthew concludes each section or begins the next section by referring to Jesus' "finishing" that particular lesson or sermon. For example, Matthew 7:28 says, "When Jesus finished these words" and Matthew 11:1 says, "When Jesus finished giving these commands." This is Matthew's way of letting us know a particular section or "book" has ended and the next section will begin.

How should I read the Gospel/treat the Gospel? Jesus is truly present in Scripture. We meet Him in a very special way in the Gospels. Therefore, the writings of the Gospels are unlike any other writing. We should read them prayerfully and with reverence and open ourselves to what God has revealed. Knowing that St. Matthew was chosen by God to be an Apostle and a Gospel writer and that he was inspired by the Holy Spirit in his writing, we should trust that his Gospel accurately conveys what Jesus said and did.

1. What do the Gospels tell us about Jesus?

   _____

   _____

2. What commission did Jesus give the Apostles? How did Matthew fulfill this commission?

   _____

   _____

3. Why do the four Gospels differ in some details?

   _____

   _____

4. For what audience was Matthew writing? _____

5. Because His audience knew the Old Testament so well, how did Matthew decide to portray Jesus in His Gospel?

   _____

6. What did Matthew do to make his case?

   _____

   _____

7. What did Matthew assume about his audience?

   _____

8. Why did Matthew organize his Gospel so neatly?

   _____

9. How many sections can Matthew's Gospel be divided into? What are the sections about?

   _____

   _____

10. How does Matthew let his reader know one section is ending and another is about to begin?

_____

11. Why are the Gospels unlike any other writing?

_____

12. Knowing that Matthew was chosen by God to be an Apostle and a Gospel writer, what should be our attitude toward his Gospel?

_____

Reflection Question

Imagine that you were one of the Apostles and felt called to write a Gospel account of Jesus' life for today's audience. What would be the most important things you'd include in the Gospel? How would you structure your Gospel? What things would you assume your audience already knows? How would you tell the story of Jesus to help people know Him and come to know and receive salvation?

_____

_____

_____

_____

_____

_____

_____

_____

_____

Parables of the Kingdom

Part I

Directions: Read the Parable of the Sower from Matthew 13:1-9 and its explanation from Matthew 13:18-23, then complete the chart below.

The Parable of the Sower

Type of ground	What happened	Meaning
1		
2		
3		
4		

Part II

Directions: Read your assigned Parable of the Kingdom, then complete the questions below.

Parable title

_____

Scripture verses

_____

Summary of the parable

_____

_____

_____

_____

_____

Meaning of the parable

_____

_____

_____

_____

_____

Jesus Fulfills God's Promises in the Old Testament

Directions: Read about how Matthew's Gospel shows how Jesus fulfills God's promises from the Old Testament, then answer the questions that follow.

Matthew begins his Gospel with a genealogy of Jesus. A genealogy is a listing of one's ancestors, or a family tree. Matthew begins Jesus' family tree with Abraham and traces it through many generations all the way to Jesus. Some of the names will seem strange to us today, but if you were a Jew living in Jesus' time, you would have instantly recognized most of them. The genealogy is an ancient literary device that draws attention to particular characters in a story. Matthew is drawing attention to who Jesus is by showing His connection to Abraham and David as well as other significant people in Salvation History. By showing this connection, Matthew invites his audience to consider how God's promises to three key Old Testament figures – Abraham, Moses, and David – are fulfilled by Jesus.

In Genesis 12:2-3, God made three amazing promises to Abraham. First, God promised Abraham that He would make of him a great nation. This promise also came with a promise of land because a nation requires land in order to exist. Second, God promised Abraham that He would make his name great. The Hebrew word for "name" refers to a dynasty of kings. The kings descended from an original king bear his name. Thus, to have a great name is to have a line of kings, or a dynasty, descend from you. Third, God promised Abraham that all the families of the earth would be blessed

by him and his descendants. God made each of these promises a covenant wtih Abraham. God formed His people through this covenant.

The first promise God made to Abraham was fulfilled by God's covenant with Moses. God called Moses to be His prophet and to speak to the people of Israel for Him. Through Moses, God freed His people from slavery in Egypt and led them to the Promised Land, where they would become a great nation. Through Moses God delivered His Law so that they would be formed into a people who would love and serve Him, the one true God, and each other. The leadership and example of Moses had a lasting impact even into the days of Jesus and beyond. St. Matthew presents Jesus as a New Moses, highlighting the many similarities between the two, but emphasizing how Jesus goes beyond anything that Moses taught or accomplished. Whereas Moses led the people on an Exodus from slavery in Egypt to freedom in the Promised Land, Jesus led all of God's people on a new exodus from slavery to death and sin to freedom in the Kingdom of God.

The second promise God made to Abraham was fulfilled by God's covenant with David. David became the first in a long line of kings, a dynasty descended from David. The kings in the line of David ruled over a great kingdom. God made many promises to David that, by the end of the Old Testament, had not been fulfilled. The Jewish people had waited for centuries for the coming of the Messiah, the one who would fulfill these promises God made to David. The Greek word for Messiah is Christ, which also means "anointed one." The Messiah, or Christ, was in fact Jesus Christ, the Son of God. But Jesus was not the first Messiah or Christ. All the kings of Israel who were descended from David were "christs," or "anointed ones." To be a king in the line of David was to be anointed by God as Israel's ruler. Therefore, to call Jesus "Christ" or "Messiah" was to refer to Him as not only the Son of God but also the Son of David, the rightful heir to the everlasting throne of David promised in God's covenant with David. All the characteristics of the Davidic covenant find their fulfillment in Jesus Christ in the everlasting New Covenant. Matthew strives to make it clear in His Gospel that Jesus is the Messiah, the Son of David, who had come to fulfill the promises God made to David in His covenant with Him. Not only does Matthew's genealogy make it known that Jesus is a descendant of David, but Matthew also emphasizes that Jesus was born in the town of Bethlehem, the birthplace of David.

Jesus would fulfill the third promise God made to Abraham and bless the world. Jesus completed God's plan of salvation and blessed the world with salvation from sin. Jesus willingly gave His life on the Cross and paid the price for sin in our place. And on the third day, Jesus rose from the dead, defeating sin and death forever, and making us sons and daughters of God once again. In the Church Jesus established during His earthly life, all mankind is invited to take part in this New Covenant and receive the blessing of salvation in Christ's Blood. Matthew's Gospel shows clearly how Jesus was the descendant of Abraham who would fulfill God's third promise to Abraham, a worldwide blessing of salvation.

1. What is a genealogy? Why does St. Matthew begin his Gospel with a genealogy?

_____

_____

2. What three things did God promise to Abraham in His covenant with him?

_____

_____

3. How did Moses fulfill God's first promise to Abraham?

_____

_____

4. How is Jesus a new Moses?

_____

5. How did David fulfill God's second promise to Abraham?

_____

_____

6. What do the words "messiah" and "christ" mean? What does it mean to call Jesus the "Messiah" or "Christ"?

_____

_____

7. How did Jesus fulfill God's third promise to David?

_____

_____

8. Recall that God made a covenant with His Chosen People, the Israelites, also known as the Hebrews, or the Jews. Jesus was Jewish. Fully God and fully man, His earthly family tree was the line of King David, which stretches back to the Father of Faith, Abraham. Many of Jesus' Disciples were Jews. It was God's plan to reveal Himself to the world through one group of people—the people of Israel—so that, when the time was right (or, "the fullness of time") His plan of salvation could be made known to the world. The plan of salvation was completed in Jesus Christ. Therefore, in the Church Jesus founded, God's chosen people become everyone who accepts Him in faith and love. We are the new Israel. Neither all Jews in Jesus' time, nor Jews who lived later, should be blamed for the crimes committed during Christ's Passion. How does Matthew's Gospel especially show us this truth?

_____

_____

_____

_____

_____

What Do We Know About Mark?

Directions: Read the Scripture passages and record the information each provides about the author of Mark's Gospel and his audience.

Part 1

1. Name? _____ or Mark (Acts 12:12).

2. His mother's name: _____ (Acts 12:12).

3. Cousin of _____ (Colossians 4:10).

4. Traveled with _____ and _____ on a missionary journey (Acts 12:25).

5. _____ and Barnabas had a disagreement about him, so Paul chose

   _____ to take with him instead (Acts 15:36-40).

6. Paul still thought Mark was helpful in _____ (2 Timothy 4:11).

7. Traveled with _____ in Rome (1 Peter 5:13).

Part 2

8. Was called the _____ of Peter by Papias in AD 135.

9. Wrote his Gospel before the destruction of the _____ in AD 70.

10. After the martyrdoms of Peter and Paul, he was believed to have become the

    _____ of Alexandria, where he was martyred.

11. His remains are thought to be buried in the large basilica in _____, Italy.

12. His feast day is _____.

Mark's Audience and Message

Part I

Directions: Use the information below to complete the note-taking template that follows.

Mark's Gospel is the shortest of the four Gospels and likely the first written. Mark tells the story of Jesus' life at a fast pace, quickly moving from one scene to the next. This gives the reader of the Gospel a sense of movement as she moves throughout the Gospel. Despite the short length of this Gospel, it often contains more details about Jesus' ministry than the others.

Mark was writing to an audience of Gentile Christians, possibly living in and around Rome. Gentiles are people of non-Jewish ethnicity – anyone who was not a Jew. This means Mark's audience was primarily non-Jewish converts to Christianity. The evidence for this fact is that Mark took the time to explain many Jewish customs that his non-Jewish readers would not have automatically understood (for example, in Mark 7:3-4, Mark explains to his reader the traditional Jewish ritual of handwashing before meals). This background information is unlike Matthew's Gospel, which was written for Jews. Matthew assumed his readers knew about Jewish customs. Further, in Mark's Gospel a Roman centurion is the first to acknowledge Jesus

as the Son of God (Mark 15:39). This makes it clear that Mark is making the case for non-Jews to believe in Jesus.

Mark likely wrote his Gospel before AD 70 because he makes no mention of the destruction of the Temple of Jerusalem, which happened in AD 70. The Temple of Jerusalem was the center of Jewish religious life and a major landmark in the city of Jerusalem. When the Romans invaded Jerusalem in AD 70, they destroyed the Temple, which was a very significant event to the Jewish people. It would likely have been mentioned in the Gospel if it had already occurred.

Mark was a disciple of St. Peter and wanted to help people in the midst of turmoil and persecution to understand Jesus better. He wanted to prepare people for the challenges of suffering and persecution. Mark uses words and phrases such as "immediately" and "at once" very often – to create a sense of urgency and of the need for repentance and action right NOW rather than waiting until it's too late. Mark also highlights Jesus' humanity and suffering, spending much time on His Passion and Death.

1. Mark's Gospel is the _____Shortest_____ of the four Gospels and likely the _____first_____ written.

2. Mark's Gospel moves at a _____fast_____ pace, but often contains more _____detail_____ about Jesus' public ministry.

3. Mark's audience: Gentile _Christians_, possibly in and around _rome_.

4. Gentiles are people of _non jewish_ ethnicity.

5. Supporting evidence: Mark explained Jewish _customs_ (Mark 7:3-4).

6. A Roman _certurion_ was the first to acknowledge Jesus as the Son of God (Mark 15:39).

7. When he wrote: before _AD 70_.

8. Supporting evidence: He makes no mention of the destruction of the _Temple of Jerusulam_ (which happened in AD 70).

9. Why he wrote: Mark was a disciple of _St Peter_.

10. He wanted to help people in the midst of turmoil and persecution to _understand_ Jesus better and to prepare them for the challenges of _Suffering_ and _Persicution_.

11. Supporting evidence: Mark uses words and phrases such as _immediately_ and _at once_ to show a sense of urgency and need for repentance and action right NOW.

12. Mark also highlights Jesus' _humanity_ and suffering, spending much time on His Passion and Death.

Part II

Directions: Look up the given Scripture passages about the main messages of Jesus and fill in the blanks.

Verse	Message
Mark 1:16-20	13. Jesus calls us all, just as He called His _disciples_.
Mark 1:11	14. Jesus is the _Son_ of God.

Verse	Message
Mark 2:9-12 Mark 4:39-41	15. Jesus performed many __miracle__.
Mark 6:34 Mark 3:5 Mark 10:21 Mark 14: 34	16. Jesus responds with human emotions including __Pity__, __anger__, __love__, and __Sorrow__.
Mark 1:15	17. Jesus teaches about the __Kingdom__ of God and that we need to __repent__ and believe in the __gospel__ to follow Him.
Mark 1:22	18. Jesus taught with __authority__.
Mark 16:5-6	19. Jesus was __rasied__ from the dead.
Mark 16:9 Mark 16:14 Mark 16:15	20. The risen Jesus appeared first to __Mary magdalene__ and then His __Commisson__ and told them to __Proclaim__ the Gospel to every creature.
Mark 16:19	21. Jesus ascended into __heaven__.

The Structure of Mark's Gospel

Directions: Look up each Scripture passage and decide which section of Mark's Gospel it best fits under and then describe why you think so.

➤ **The Preparation for the Public Ministry of Jesus** – The ministry of John the Baptist, the Baptism of Jesus, Jesus is tempted in the desert.

➤ **The Mystery of Jesus** – Jesus calls the Apostles, cures people and casts out demons, and teaches about the Kingdom of God.

➤ **The Mystery Begins to Be Revealed** – Jesus asks who people say that He is, begins to predict His Death, is Transfigured, and moves toward Jerusalem and His Passion.

➤ **The Full Revelation of the Mystery** – The priests try to find ways to trap Jesus; Jesus' Passion, Death, and Resurrection; and everything becomes clear to the Apostles.

	Passage	Which section?	Why?
1	Mark 14:22-26		
2	Mark 1:6-8		
3	Mark 9:2-8		

	Passage	Which section?	Why?
4	Mark 6:34-44		
5	Mark 11:7-10		
6	Mark 4:1-9		
7	Mark 8:27-30		
8	Mark 14:32-34		
9	Mark 3:1-5		
10	Mark 16:19		

Introduction to the Gospel of Luke Note-Taking Guide

Directions: Fill in the blanks to complete the note-taking guide during the class discussion.

1. Luke's Gospel is the most _____ of the four Gospels.

2. Luke wrote his Gospel for a man named _____.

3. Luke himself explains that he has written an "orderly sequence" after "_____ accurately everything anew."

4. Luke's Gospel is the only Gospel to claim to be written _____.

5. _____ is the traditional author of Luke's Gospel, and he was a traveling companion of _____.

6. The author of Luke was a _____ convert to Christianity, which makes him the only Gospel writer who was not a _____.

7. _____ was a likely source for Luke's Gospel.

8. Luke contains the most complete version of the _____ and _____ narratives of Jesus, including many details only _____ would have known.

9. Luke's audience was _____.

10. Luke's Gospel was focused on Jesus' ministry to _____.

11. He emphasized that Gentiles did not have to become _____ first in order to believe in _____.

12. Luke's Gospel is also known as the Gospel of _____.

13. Luke's Gospel stresses the importance of _____ and the working of the _____.

14. Most scholars believe Luke's Gospel was written after the destruction of _____.

15. It is likely that the Gospel of Luke was written around AD _____.

The Structure of Luke's Gospel

Directions: Look up each Scripture passage and decide which section of Luke's Gospel it best fits under. Then briefly summarize the passage and describe why you think it belongs in that section.

› **The Prologue and Infancy Narrative.**
› **The Preparation for and Ministry in Galilee.**
› **The Journey to and Teaching Ministry in Jerusalem.**
› **The Passion and Resurrection Narrative.**

Passage	Which section?	Why?
1 Luke 1:26-38		
2 Luke 3:21-22		
3 Luke 11:1-4		
4 Luke 22:14-20		

Passage	Which section?	Why?
5 Luke 6:17-26		
6 Luke 8:22-25		
7 Luke 23:33-43		
8 Luke 19:28-40		
9 Luke 2:1-7		
10 Luke 24:1-12		

Scenes from Luke

The Annunciation, by Giorgio Vasari. Musée du Louvre, Paris.

The Visitation, by Giotto.
Cappella Scrovegni (Arena Chapel), Padua.

The Adoration of the Shepherds,
by Gerard van Honthorst.
Wallraf-Richartz Museum, Cologne.

What Does Luke Teach Us about Our Mother?

Directions: Read the following excerpts from the Gospel of Luke about Mary and answer the focus and reflection questions.

> Announcement of the Birth of Jesus (Luke 1:26-38).

> Mary Visits Elizabeth (Luke 1:39-45).

> The Canticle of Mary (Luke 1:46-56).

> The Birth of Jesus (Luke 2:1-7).

> The Visit of the Shepherds (Luke 2:15-19).

> From the Presentation (Luke 2:33-35).

> The Boy Jesus in the Temple (Luke 2:41-52).

1. Based on the readings, what are three qualities you would use to describe Mary? Be sure to provide evidence from the readings to support your claim.

   _____

   _____

   _____

2. In the readings, twice it says that "Mary kept all these things in her heart." What do you think this means?

   _____

   _____

   _____

3. Mary was a virgin, and remained a virgin throughout her life. What evidence in these readings supports this belief?

   _____

   _____

   _____

4. The Catholic Church believes Mary was conceived without Original Sin. What evidence in the readings supports this belief?

_____

_____

_____

5. Mary is also called the Mother of God. What evidence in the readings supports this belief?

_____

_____

_____

6. What is the first thing Mary does when she finds out she is pregnant with Jesus? How is this connected with our own call to evangelize?

_____

_____

_____

7. What does the Canticle of Mary teach us about who God is and how we are called to relate to Him?

_____

_____

_____

8. Based on the readings, what does Mary's life teach us for our own lives?

_____

_____

_____

Exploring the Theme of Mercy in Luke's Gospel

Directions: Read the following passages from Luke's Gospel, then answer the questions that follow.

The Pardon of the Sinful Woman (Luke 7:36-50).

The Parable of the Lost Son (Luke 15:11-32).

The Repentant Thief (Luke 23:39-43).

1. Briefly summarize what takes place in the first passage.

    _____

    _____

    _____

2. Briefly summarize what takes place in the second passage.

    _____

    _____

    _____

3. Briefly summarize what takes place in the third passage.

    _____

    _____

    _____

4. What do all three passages have in common?

    _____

    _____

    _____

5. What do all three passages teach us about the mercy and forgiveness of Jesus?

_____

_____

_____

6. Based on these three passages, what seems to be required in order to be forgiven by God?

_____

_____

_____

7. The Gospel of Luke is also referred to as the Gospel of Mercy. Why is this a fitting name for this Gospel?

_____

_____

_____

8. Pope Francis has said that "God never tires of forgiving us; rather it is us who tire of seeking His mercy." How is this quote exemplified by the Gospel of Luke?

_____

_____

_____

Scriptural Divine Mercy Chaplet

Directions: Pray the Divine Mercy Chaplet together as a class. At the beginning of each decade, read the passages from Luke 23.

Begin by praying the Our Father, Hail Mary, and Apostles Creed.

First Decade (Luke 23:1-16)

Then the whole assembly of them arose and brought him before Pilate. They brought charges against him, saying, "We found this man misleading our people; he opposes the payment of taxes to Caesar and maintains that he is the Messiah, a king." Pilate asked him, "Are you the king of the Jews?" He said to him in reply, "You say so." Pilate then addressed the chief priests and the crowds, "I find this man not guilty." But they were adamant and said, "He is inciting the people with his teaching throughout all Judea, from Galilee where he began even to here." On hearing this Pilate asked if the man was a Galilean; and upon learning that he was under Herod's jurisdiction, he sent him to Herod who was in Jerusalem at that time. Herod was very glad to see Jesus; he had been wanting to see him for a long time, for he had heard about him and had been hoping to see him perform some sign. He questioned him at length, but he gave him no answer. The chief priests and scribes, meanwhile, stood by accusing him harshly. [Even] Herod and his soldiers treated him contemptuously and mocked him, and after clothing him in resplendent garb, he sent him back to Pilate. Herod and Pilate became friends that very day, even though they had been enemies formerly. Pilate then summoned the chief priests, the rulers, and the people and said to them, "You brought this man to me and accused him of inciting the people to revolt. I have conducted my investigation in your presence and have not found this man guilty of the charges you have brought against him, nor did Herod, for he sent him back to us. So no capital crime has been committed by him. Therefore I shall have him flogged and then release him."

(Large bead)   **Leader:** *Eternal Father, we offer to you the body and blood, soul and divinity, of your dearly beloved Son, our Lord Jesus Christ...*

Response: *In atonement for our sins and those of the whole world.*

(Smaller beads)   **Leader:** *For the sake of His sorrowful Passion...*

Response: *Have mercy on us and on the whole world.* (10 times)

Second Decade (Luke 23:18-25)

But all together they shouted out, "Away with this man! Release Barabbas to us." (Now Barabbas had been imprisoned for a rebellion that had taken place in the city and for murder.) Again Pilate addressed them, still wishing to release Jesus, but they continued their shouting, "Crucify him! Crucify him!" Pilate addressed them a third time, "What evil has this man done? I found him guilty of no capital crime. Therefore I shall have him flogged and then release him." With loud shouts, however, they persisted in calling for his crucifixion, and their voices prevailed. The verdict of Pilate was that their demand should be granted. So he released the man who had been imprisoned for rebellion and murder, for whom they asked, and he handed Jesus over to them to deal with as they wished.

(Large bead) **Leader:** *Eternal Father, we offer to you the body and blood, soul and divinity, of your dearly beloved Son, our Lord Jesus Christ...*

Response: *In atonement for our sins and those of the whole world.*

(Smaller beads) **Leader:** *For the sake of His sorrowful Passion...*

Response: *Have mercy on us and on the whole world.* (10 times)

Third Decade (Luke 23:26-32)

As they led him away they took hold of a certain Simon, a Cyrenian, who was coming in from the country; and after laying the cross on him, they made him carry it behind Jesus. A large crowd of people followed Jesus, including many women who mourned and lamented him. Jesus turned to them and said, "Daughters of Jerusalem, do not weep for me; weep instead for yourselves and for your children, for indeed, the days are coming when people will say, 'Blessed are the barren, the wombs that never bore and the breasts that never nursed.' At that time people will say to the mountains, 'Fall upon us!' and to the hills, 'Cover us!' for if these things are done when the wood is green what will happen when it is dry?" Now two others, both criminals, were led away with him to be executed.

(Large bead) **Leader:** *Eternal Father, we offer to you the body and blood, soul and divinity, of your dearly beloved Son, our Lord Jesus Christ...*

Response: *In atonement for our sins and those of the whole world.*

(Smaller beads) **Leader:** *For the sake of His sorrowful Passion...*

Response: *Have mercy on us and on the whole world.* (10 times)

Fourth Decade (Luke 23:33-43)

When they came to the place called the Skull, they crucified him and the criminals there, one on his right, the other on his left. [Then Jesus said, "Father, forgive them, they know not what they do."] They divided his garments by casting lots. The people stood by and watched; the rulers, meanwhile, sneered at him and said, "He saved others, let him save himself if he is the chosen one, the Messiah of God." Even the soldiers jeered at him. As they approached to offer him wine they called out, "If you are King of the Jews, save yourself." Above him there was an inscription that read, "This is the King of the Jews." Now one of the criminals hanging there reviled Jesus, saying, "Are you not the Messiah? Save yourself and us." The other, however, rebuking him, said in reply, "Have you no fear of God, for you are subject to the same condemnation? And indeed, we have been condemned justly, for the sentence we received corresponds to our crimes, but this man has done nothing criminal." Then he said, "Jesus, remember me when you come into your kingdom." He replied to him, "Amen, I say to you, today you will be with me in Paradise."

(Large bead)   **Leader:** *Eternal Father, we offer to you the body and blood, soul and divinity, of your dearly beloved Son, our Lord Jesus Christ...*

Response: *In atonement for our sins and those of the whole world.*

(Smaller beads)   **Leader:** *For the sake of His sorrowful Passion...*

Response: *Have mercy on us and on the whole world.* (10 times)

Fifth Decade (Luke 23:44-49)

It was now about noon and darkness came over the whole land until three in the afternoon because of an eclipse of the sun. Then the veil of the temple was torn down the middle. Jesus cried out in a loud voice, "Father, into your hands I commend my spirit"; and when he had said this he breathed his last. The centurion who witnessed what had happened glorified God and said, "This man was innocent beyond doubt." When all the people who had gathered for this spectacle saw what had happened, they returned home beating their breasts; but all his acquaintances stood at a distance, including the women who had followed him from Galilee and saw these events.

(Large bead)   **Leader:** *Eternal Father, we offer to you the body and blood, soul and divinity, of your dearly beloved Son, our Lord Jesus Christ...*

Response: *In atonement for our sins and those of the whole world.*

(Smaller beads)   **Leader:** *For the sake of His sorrowful Passion...*

Response: *Have mercy on us and on the whole world.* (10 times)

Finish the prayer by saying:

Holy God, Holy Mighty One, Holy Immortal One, have mercy on us and on the whole world.
(3 times)

Jesus, I trust in you. (3 times)

John and the Other Gospels

Directions: Read the list of events below. In the space provided next to each event, write "J" if it is described only in John's Gospel or "S" if it happened in one or more of the Synoptic Gospels.

_____   1.   Jesus institutes the Eucharist at the Last Supper.

_____   2.   Jesus uses parables to get His point across.

_____   3.   The Miracle at the Wedding Feast at Cana.

_____   4.   The Baptism of Jesus.

_____   5.   The Raising of Lazarus.

_____   6.   Jesus' encounters the Samaritan woman at the well.

_____   7.   The Transfiguration.

_____   8.   The Pharisees bring to Jesus the woman caught in adultery and insist that she be stoned.

_____   9.   The Bread of Life discourse.

_____   10.   Jesus performs exorcisms.

_____   11.   Infancy narratives (stories of Jesus' birth and childhood).

_____   12.   Healing of the crippled man at the Pool at Bethesda.

_____   13.   Healing of the blind man at the Pool of Siloam.

_____   14.   Peter's confession of faith and Jesus giving him the keys.

_____   15.   Jesus' encounter with Nicodemus.

Introduction to the Gospel of John Note-Taking Guide

Directions: Fill in the blanks to complete the note-taking guide during the class discussion.

1. The traditional author of John's Gospel is _____, who was one of the

    _____ and was the _____ whom Jesus was

    closest to.

2. The author of John was present at the foot of the _____, and it was to

    him that Jesus entrusted the care of His _____ after His Death.

3. John's Gospel was likely written between AD _____ and

    _____.

4. John's Gospel presents the story of Jesus' life from an _____

    perspective and presents a more developed _____ understanding of
    who Christ is.

5. John's Gospel does not present a merely _____ or

    _____ retelling of Christ's life.

6. The ending of John's Gospel states that there were many other _____
    of Jesus not included in this book.

7. The purpose of John's Gospel was to reveal deeper _____ about

    Christ's life so that his readers might believe that Jesus is the _____

    and the _____ of God and through their belief have

    _____ life.

8. In contrast to the other, Synoptic Gospels, John's Gospel is very

    _____, _____,

    and _____.

9. John's Gospel is told not in a _____ way, but in a way that

    reveals that Jesus is the Incarnate _____ of God who has always

    _____ with God.

10. John's audience was primarily _____.

11. John's Gospel helped combat many false ideas about who Jesus was by presenting His full

    _____ and full _____.

12. John develops a more complete _____, or theology of Christ.

13. John devotes a large portion of his Gospel to Jesus' teachings at the

    _____, which interpret the meaning of His

    _____, Death, and _____.

14. The narrative of John's Gospel focuses on seven _____, or

    _____ deeds.

15. The movement from dialogue to _____ in Christ's teachings

    emphasizes that His teachings are now meant for the entire _____.

Jesus' I AM Statements

Directions: Read the following passages from John's Gospel and fill in the seven "I AM" statements that Jesus makes in the Gospel of John.

1. John 6:47-51 – I AM _____

2. John 8:12 – I AM _____

3. John 10:7-15 (Hint: There are two here.)

    I AM _____

    and I AM _____

4. John 11:17-27 – I AM _____

5. John 14:5-7 – I AM _____

6. John 15: 1-5 – I AM _____

The Seven Signs of John's Gospel

Directions: Read each of the following passages. Briefly summarize the passage in your words and then identify which one of the seven signs is represented in the passage. Finally, answer the questions that follow.

	Passage	Summary	Sign
1	John 2:1-11		
2	John 4:46-54		
3	John 5:1-18		
4	John 6:1-15		
5	John 6:16-21		

	Passage	Summary	Sign
6	John 9:1-41		
7	John 11:1-54		

Reflection Questions

1. What do these signs together reveal to us about Jesus and His mission?

   _____

   _____

   _____

   _____

2. Which of the signs do you find to be the most meaningful? Why?

   _____

   _____

   _____

   _____

Nativity

BY JEAN-BAPTISTE MARIE PIERRE (18TH CENTURY)

In private collection, courtesy Web Gallery of Art.

In the Beginning Was the Word

Directions: Read the prologue to John's Gospel, John 1:1-18, then read the brief essay about the prologue. Finally, answer the questions that follow.

John's Prologue

The Gospel of John begins very differently from the other Gospels. The first chapter of John, known as the prologue, is written in a very poetic manner like the overture to an opera or symphony. Within this first chapter the important themes that will be unpacked throughout the rest of the Gospel are introduced. In a certain sense the first chapter of John is like the entire Gospel in miniature.

The first chapter shows us that St. John is very concerned with showing Christ to be the new Adam. He borrows the very first line of the book of Genesis to tell the story of the birth of Christ, "In the beginning..." Many of the themes found in the creation story of Genesis are also present in John's prologue, such as the themes of light and darkness, the creation of life, and the power of God's Word.

The central figure of John's prologue is the Word of God who assumed a human nature. In revealing the Word to us, John doesn't just take his reader back to the beginning of time. He goes further and takes us to before the beginning of the created world. The Word of God who becomes man, John tells us, existed before creation itself. The Word of God, Jesus Christ, is God Himself. All things came into existence through the Word, and the Word fully revealed God to the world.

John's teaching about the Word helps us to understand the mystery of the Trinity. It is clear that the "Word" is a distinct Person from the Father. But John also makes clear that the "Word" is one with the Father. John reveals to us the first two Persons of the Trinity, God the Father and God the Son.

1. Who is the "Word" John is referring to? What are three things John says about the Word?

   _____

   _____

2. Which John is referred to in John's prologue? What did he do?

   _____

   _____

3. What is this whole first chapter a summary of? What themes from John's Gospel are introduced in this first chapter?

_____

_____

4. How did most people react to the "Light" or the "Word"?

_____

5. What is promised to those who accept the "Word"?

_____

6. How is the prologue to John's Gospel connected to the Creation story in Genesis?

_____

_____

7. How does John's prologue teach us about the mystery of the Trinity?

_____

_____

Reflection Question

Choose one of the seven signs from John's Gospel and write a five- to seven-sentence paragraph about how that sign is connected to or foreshadowed in the prologue to John's Gospel.

_____

_____

_____

_____

_____

The Sacraments

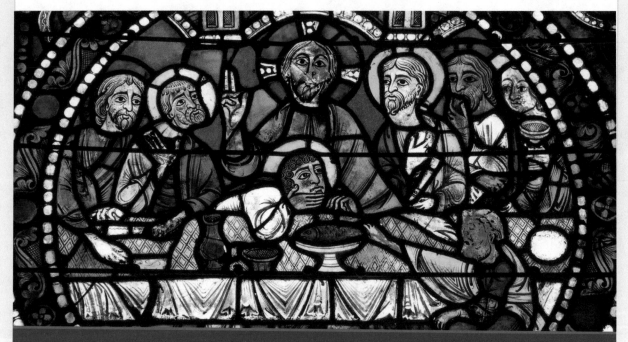

In this unit, you will learn about...

> The nature of the Sacraments.

> The history, celebration, effects, and living of the Sacrament of Baptism.

> The history, celebration, effects, and living of the Sacrament of Confirmation.

> The history, celebration, effects, and living of the Sacrament of Holy Eucharist.

> The history, celebration, effects, and living of the Sacrament of Penance and Reconciliation.

> The history, celebration, effects, and living of the Sacrament of Anointing of the Sick.

> The history, celebration, effects, and living of the Sacrament of Holy Matrimony.

> The history, celebration, effects, and living of the Sacrament of Holy Orders.

Image courtesy FORGET Patrick/SAGAPHOTO.COM / Alamy Stock Photo

Introduction

A Sacrament is a sign of God's grace that brings about the grace it signifies. The Sacraments of the Church are at once visible and invisible. Jesus established the seven Sacraments of the Church during His earthly life: Baptism, Confirmation, Holy Eucharist, Penance and Reconciliation, Anointing of the Sick, Holy Orders, and Holy Matrimony. These seven signs of grace each consist of two parts necessary for validity: *matter* and *form*. The matter consists of water, bread, wine, oil, hands, speech, or other material elements involved in giving grace. The form consists of words or actions that express the circumstances of that giving and celebrate them as a priestly community of ministers.

The Sacraments can be arranged into three categories: the Sacraments of Initiation, the Sacraments of Healing, and the Sacraments at the Service of Communion. The Sacraments of Initiation are Baptism, Confirmation, and Holy Eucharist. Together, they make us full members of the Church, pour out the Holy Spirit within our souls, and nourish us for Christian life. They give to us a particular missionary task, to make disciples of all the nations, and strengthen us for this work. The Eucharist, in a special way, is the source and summit of our Christian faith. In this Sacrament, the Lord Himself is really present to us, Body and Blood, Soul and Divinity. By receiving the Eucharist, we participate in Christ's saving sacrifice and evangelizing mission.

The Sacraments of Healing are Penance and Reconciliation and Anointing of the Sick. By these Sacraments, we are healed of sin and our relationship to God and His Church is restored. Anointing of the Sick, in a special way, can heal the body of illness and suffering, or, if that is not God's will, prepare the person for their final journey in life, passing from this life to the next. These Sacraments help to unite our suffering with the redemptive suffering of Christ on the Cross.

The Sacraments at the Service of Communion are Holy Orders and Holy Matrimony. Through these Sacraments, Jesus makes us his associates in special missions to give our lives for the salvation of others. In Holy Orders, men are ordained to the priesthood or deaconate to serve the Church and care for the People of God. In Holy Matrimony, one man and one woman are united in marriage to love and serve God, each other, and their children.

Are there any questions you still have about the topics you learned last month? What steps can you take to find out the answers?

_____

_____

_____

_____

What questions do you have right now about the topics you will be learning about in this unit?

_____

_____

_____

_____

Unit 3 Vocabulary

Anointing: Rubbing or marking with oil. Holy oil is spread on our foreheads in Baptism and Confirmation, and again in the Sacrament of Anointing of the Sick.

Baptism of Desire: A Catechumen, or a person who is preparing to be baptized, who dies before receiving Baptism is assured salvation through her desire for Baptism, repentance for sin, and charity.

Body of Christ: The People of God make up the Body of Christ. A body has many parts, just like the People of God is made up of different people with different gifts and talents. Though we are all different, as the Body of Christ we are one body with Christ as our head. Also refers to the consecrated Communion host we receive in the Eucharist, which is the true Body and Blood, Soul and Divinity of Christ.

Catechumen: A person who is preparing to receive the Sacrament of Baptism and become a member of the Catholic Church by receiving training in Christian teaching and practice.

Commemorate: To celebrate the memory of something. The Sacraments commemorate Christ's Passion.

Conversion: Turning away from sin and returning to God. It is the first step in the Sacrament of Penance and Reconciliation. We recognize all that we have done to hurt our heavenly Father and are truly sorry for our actions to hurt our heavenly Father, are truly sorry for our sins, and resolve not to sin again. The examination of conscience can aid us in recognizing our faults.

Divine Physician: A title for Jesus that describes how He came to call sinners, not the righteous. This is similar to the way a physician or doctor treats those who are sick, not those who are healthy.

Efficacious: Effective, or possessing the ability to cause an effect. The Sacraments cause the grace of God, of which they are also signs.

Gifts of the Holy Spirit: Wisdom, knowledge, understanding, counsel, fortitude, piety, and fear of the Lord. The anointing in Confirmation is a sign of receiving these gifts.

Grace: The free and undeserved gift of God's life within us. The Sacraments are efficacious signs of God's grace.

In Persona Christi Capitis: In the Person of Christ the Head. When an ordained priest performs his priestly function—for example, when consecrating the Eucharist—he is no longer working as himself, but rather, "in the person of Christ the Head." When we say "the Head," we mean the Head of the Church. It is not the priest who transforms the bread and wine into the Body and Blood of Christ, but rather, Jesus Himself, working in and through the priest.

Indelible Mark: A permanent, un-removable spiritual seal or mark placed on our souls by God in the Sacraments of Baptism and Confirmation, and upon those who receive the Sacrament of Holy Orders, that set us apart as belonging to God. The baptismal seal allows us to participate in the Mass, and use the Gifts of the Holy Spirit to live lives of holiness. The seal of Confirmation strengthens us to be witnesses of the Gospel in the battle between good and evil waged all around us.

Indissoluble: Incapable of being undone or broken; permanent. Because it is a total gift of self, the bond of marriage is unbreakable and permanent.

Inheritance: Gifts a person receives from someone in the family who has died, or traits received from one's parents. By our Baptism, we have an inheritance with Christ, which means that as adopted children of God, we receive gifts from Him and that we will be like Him.

Lamb of God: A title given to Jesus that describes His sacrifice to free us from sin. Just like the sacrifice of the Passover lamb freed the Israelites from slavery, Jesus' sacrifice frees us from death and sin in a new Passover.

Ministerial Priesthood: The ordained priesthood who share in the priesthood of Christ by acting *in persona Christi capitas,* that is, in the person of Christ, the head. These men do not preach, sanctify, and govern by the own authority, but rather, by the authority given them by Christ, the head of the Church, to act in His person.

Mortal sin: Serious sin that we choose to commit even though we know it is wrong. Mortal sin separates us from God and completely rejects His love for us.

Original Sin: The first sin of Adam and Eve that brought pain, suffering, and death into the world. Because we are all descendants of Adam and Eve we are all born with Original Sin in our souls. We need to be baptized to remove the stain of Original Sin. The effects of Original Sin remain, however. For example, we tend to sin, we suffer, and die.

Passover: The central event of the Exodus. The final plague God sent upon Egypt was the plague of the death of the first born of every family in Egypt. By sacrificing a lamb, spreading its blood on their doorposts, and eating its roasted flesh in a sacred meal of bread and wine, the Israelite homes would be passed over by the plague of death. God also commanded that the Israelites remember this original Passover event every year with a memorial meal. The original Passover foreshadows Christ's own sacrifice on the Cross.

Primordial: Existing from the very beginning. Marriage is called the "primordial sacrament" because, though it was not a Sacrament until the age of the Church, marriage between one man and one woman has existed from the very beginning of human existence.

Redemptive: Acting to save or free someone. Christ's Suffering and Death on the Cross saved us from sin and freed us from death.

Sacrament: A sign of God's grace that gives the grace that it signifies. Jesus founded seven Sacraments: Baptism, Confirmation, Holy Eucharist, Penance and Reconciliation, Anointing of the Sick, Holy Orders, and Holy Matrimony.

Venial sin: Less serious sin that hurts our relationship with God, but does not destroy it.

Witness: Someone who sees something happen and tells others about what he saw. We are called to be witnesses of Christ to the world.

Chartres Cathedral Photo Collage
(EXTERIOR)

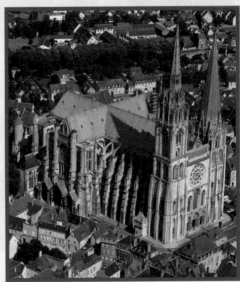

Photo courtesy Kent G. Becker.

Chartres Cathedral Photo Collage
(INTERIOR)

Photo courtesy Kent G. Becker.

Photo courtesy Kent G. Becker.

Chartres Cathedral Photo Collage
(STAINED GLASS)

Stained glass window detail. Photo by Paul Williams.

Chartres Cathedral Photo Collage
(PLAN VIEW)

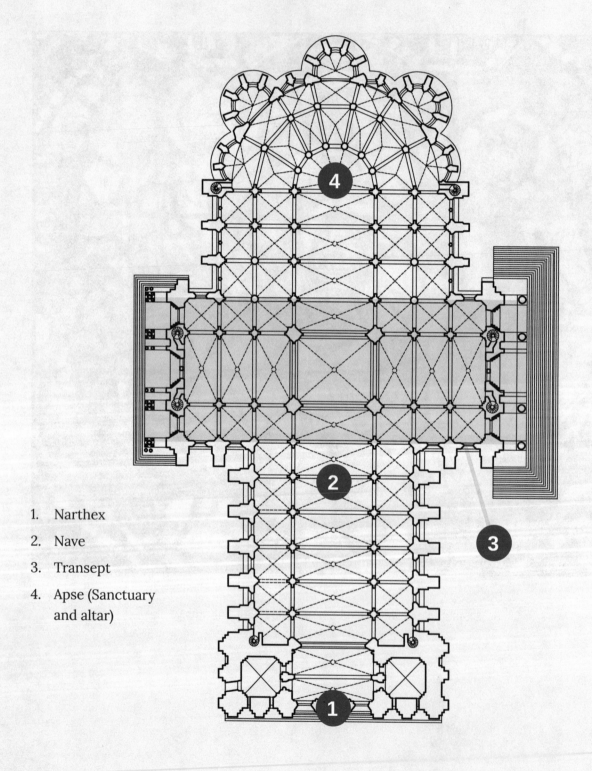

1. Narthex
2. Nave
3. Transept
4. Apse (Sanctuary and altar)

Chartres Cathedral Photo Collage

Directions: Take some time to quietly view and reflect on the photographs. Then discuss the questions below with your classmates.

Conversation Questions

1. These are photographs of the Cathedral of Notre Dame de Chartres. This cathedral was built in 1193 and is an example of Gothic architecture. What does Notre Dame de Chartres mean?

2. Find Chartres, France, on a map or globe.

Exterior

3. How would you describe the exterior (outside) of the cathedral? Why do you think cathedrals are built facing east?

4. Does Chartres cathedral look similar to or different from the church where you attend Mass? How would celebrating Mass in a place like this be different from Mass at your parish?

5. The photo in the lower left corner of the exterior page is a detail of the sculpture over one of the entrances to the cathedral known as the Royal Portal. Who is the central figure? Why do you think these entrances are called portals?

Interior

6. At each Holy Mass, Heaven and earth meet. What are some ways the interior of this cathedral communicates this reality?

7. Why do we light candles in churches? What do the candles signify?

Stained glass

8. Chartres Cathedral is famous for its 12th- to 14th-century stained glass. This detail is from one of the windows. What event from Jesus' life does it show?

9. All the natural light that enters Chartres Cathedral is filtered through stained glass. What effect do you think that has on the experience of being inside the cathedral?

Plan View

10. Find the different spaces of the cathedral: the narthex, the nave, the transept, and the sanctuary. The narthex was reserved for catechumens – those who had not been fully initiated into the Church. Why do you think the narthex is located where it is in relation to the nave and the altar?

11. How does the architecture of the building communicate where the most sacred space can be found?

The Sacraments Make the Invisible Visible

Directions: Answer the questions below.

1. A Sacrament is an outward and visible sign of an inward and invisible grace.
   Put this quotation in your own words:

   _____

   _____

   _____

2. The Church is both visible and invisble; material and divine. The Church helps us get to
   Heaven, and also gives us a taste of what Heaven will be like. In what ways do the art and
   architecture of Chartres Cathedral – a church – represent the Church?

   _____

   _____

   _____

3. The Seven Sacraments are Baptism, Confirmation, Eucharist, Penance and Reconciliation,
   Anointing of the Sick, Marriage, and Holy Orders. The *Catechism* teaches that the Church
   herself is also a Sacrament. Why do you think that is?

   _____

   _____

   _____

Mond Crucifixion

BY RAPHAEL (1502)

National Gallery, London.

Mond Crucifixion

Mond Crucifixion, *by Raphael (1502)*

Directions: Take some time to quietly view and reflect on the art. Let yourself be inspired in any way that happens naturally. Then think about the questions below, and discuss them with your classmates.

Discussion Questions

1. How would you describe this scene as Raphael has painted it? What adjectives would you use?

2. What feelings does this painting seem intended to inspire?

3. Who or what are the liveliest figures in the painting? Where are they?

4. What do you think the sun and the moon represent?

5. Is this painting like other depictions of the Crucifixion you have seen? How is it similar? How is it different?

6. Does Jesus appear to be suffering, or does He appear to be at peace?

7. Who are the people with Jesus?

8. There are angels on either side of Jesus. What are they doing?

9. This painting by Renaissance artist Raphael was part of an altarpiece. Why is a painting like this appropriate for an altar?

Matthew 19:6

So they are no longer two, but one flesh.
Therefore, what God has joined together,
no human being must separate.

Matthew 26:26

While they were eating, Jesus took bread, said the blessing, broke it, and giving it to his disciples said, "Take and eat; this is my body."

Matthew 28:19-20

Go, therefore, and make disciples of all nations, baptizing them in the name of the Father, and of the Son, and of the holy Spirit, teaching them to observe all that I have commanded you.

John 20:23

Whose sins you forgive are forgiven them,
and whose sins you retain are retained.

Acts 13:2-3

While they were worshiping the Lord and fasting, the holy Spirit said, "Set apart for me Barnabas and Saul for the work to which I have called them." Then, completing their fasting and prayer, they laid hands on them and sent them off.

_____

_____

_____

_____

_____

_____

_____

_____

_____

Acts 19:6

And when Paul laid [his] hands on them, the holy Spirit came upon them, and they spoke in tongues and prophesied.

James 5:14-15

Is anyone among you sick? He should summon the presbyters of the church, and they should pray over him and anoint [him] with oil in the name of the Lord, and the prayer of faith will save the sick person, and the Lord will raise him up. If he has committed any sins, he will be forgiven.

What Is a Sacrament?

Directions: Read the essay below, and on your own paper, make an outline of the key points. Then answer the questions that follow.

You may have heard the expression "God is love." Examine that sentence carefully, and you will see that love is not something that God does; love is what God is. He is the Blessed Trinity: one God in three Persons. This means that God is a communion of Persons—an unbreakable bond of life-giving love.

Jesus is God the Son, and His whole mission is one of love. When you love someone, you want what is good for him or her. The best thing for everyone is to live a holy life and to get to Heaven. Jesus lived, died, and was resurrected to open Heaven to us so we could be with God there.

When Jesus was on earth, He spent time with many people. He showed them love in many ways, sometimes just by talking with them. He also shared meals with them, touched them, and healed them.

Jesus is not here on Earth with us in the same way he was in the time of the Apostles, but He is still here. He is with you, and will never abandon you. And He has given you seven very special ways you can share in His life of love. These are called the Sacraments.

What Are the Seven Sacraments?

Jesus Christ instituted seven Sacraments. He entrusted them to the Church to administer them to His people throughout the ages after He ascended into Heaven. God's grace is necessary for us to get to Heaven and to become holier. We cannot do either of those things by ourselves. Therefore, it is necessary for us to receive the Sacraments in order to receive God's grace.

The water of Baptism makes us sons and daughters of God. The Holy Spirit is strengthened within us in Confirmation. We receive the Body and Blood of Jesus Christ under the appearance of bread and wine in the Eucharist. Our sins against God and His Church are forgiven in Penance and Reconciliation. The sick are blessed in Anointing of the Sick. A man and woman become united in love and open themselves to the gift of life in Matrimony. Called men are ordained priests, servants of God's love, in Holy Orders.

These are the Sacraments of the Church. Even in this short explanation, it is easy to see how the grace of God is revealed in these signs and symbols.

The Sacraments Do What They Say They Do

But the Sacraments are much more than signs and symbols. The Sacraments do what they say they do. For example, Baptism isn't just a "symbolic" cleansing of sin; it is an actual cleansing of the stain of Original Sin that makes you a child of God and leaves an indelible mark on your soul. We encounter

Jesus in a real and special way in all the Sacraments. This effectiveness is what we mean we say the Sacraments are "efficacious signs of grace." That grace is a sign of God's love, which He gives you freely, and not because you've done anything to earn or deserve it.

Remember, love is not just something that God does; it is what He is. Through the work of the Holy Spirit and His ministers in the Church, Jesus shares meals with you, touches you, heals you, and shares His divine life with you in the Sacraments. The *Catechism* explains, "As fire transforms into itself everything it touches, so the Holy Spirit transforms into the divine life whatever is subjected to his power" (CCC 1127). The grace you receive in the Sacraments transforms you and, with your cooperation, helps you be like your Heavenly Father and be with Him in Heaven.

1. What does it mean to say God is love?

   It tells us that love is not a thing god does but it is who he is

2. What does the Blessed Trinity teach us about who God is?

   It shows us "that gods love for us is unbreakable

3. What is a Sacrament?

   they are ways that jesus can share his life and love with us

4. Why did Jesus institute the Sacraments?

   to help us reach heaven

5. What are the Seven Sacraments?

   Baptisim, Conformation, Eucharist, Pentance and recon -cileation, Acointing the sick, Matrimony

6. How are the Sacraments different from other signs and symbols?

   they actully do what they say they do

7. The *Catechism* explains, "Celebrated worthily in faith, the sacraments confer the grace that they signify. They are *efficacious* because in them Christ himself is at work: it is he who baptizes, he who acts in his sacraments in order to communicate the grace that each sacrament signifies." (1127)

How would you put this statement into your own words?

Sacraments provide virtues from God and they work
to produce the disired effect because they come directly
from God. It is God who is working through the
Sacraments

Reflection Question

Our culture places a high priority on rewarding hard work. Working hard in school helps you achieve good grades. Working hard at soccer practice helps you play better. Working hard at a job might earn you a higher salary. Can you "earn" or "achieve" any of the Sacraments? Why or why not?

It depends on which Sacrament because their all different.
For Example you might work for marriage because of
all the preparations but you would not work for a different
Sacrament such as baptisim

Celebrations and Sacraments

Directions: Write a summary paragraph explaining the difference between ordinary rituals or celebrations and Sacraments.

Celebrations and other rituals are things we do for celebration It does not bestow anything upon us. Sacrament happen once in a life time and bestow upon us Gods grace.

Great God by Leonardo Alenza.

Sacraments Help Us Live Like the Lord

Directions: Fill in the chart with information you already know about the Sacraments. It's okay if you have to leave some sections blank.

Sacrament	How does this Sacrament show God's self-giving love?	How does receiving this Sacrament help me become more like my Heavenly Father?	Questions I still have about this Sacrament
Baptism	It rids us of our sins with the holy water	It cleanses us so we may be like him	
Confirmation	It gives us the body and blood of christ	we now have the blood and body of christ with us	
Eucharist			

Sacrament	How does this Sacrament show God's self-giving love?	How does receiving this Sacrament help me become more like my Heavenly Father?	Questions I still have about this Sacrament
Penance and Reconciliation			
Anointing of the Sick			
Marriage			
Holy Orders			

Baptism Pre-Assessment

Directions: In the left-hand column mark each statement true or false. Mark them again in the right column at the end of our study of Baptism to see if you were right.

Before beginning
your study

At the end of
your study

True or False?	**Statement**	**True or False?**
True	1. Jesus Himself was baptized.	True
True	2. A priest is the ordinary minister of Baptism.	True
True	3. Baptism forgives sin, including Original Sin.	True
False	4. A person who has never heard of Jesus but seeks truth and to do God's will can be saved from sin without Baptism.	False
False	5. You should be baptized again if you commit a serious sin.	False
False	6. Baptism is a ceremony affirming that a baby is now part of the community.	False
False	7. Scripture supports the practice of baptizing babies.	True
True	8. The Church offers Baptism to those who would like to receive it, but it is not truly necessary to the Christian life.	True

The Story of Baptism

Directions: Read the essay, then answer the questions that follow.

At the Last Supper, Jesus told St. Peter, "Unless I wash you, you will have no inheritance with me" (John 13:8). What did He mean?

To understand, we first have to know what an inheritance is. Often, we use the word to mean gifts that a person receives from someone in the family who has died. A second meaning of the word can be traits we receive from our parents—you might have inherited your mother's eye color or your father's hair color, for example. Jesus intended both of these meanings in a certain way. To have an inheritance with Jesus means we receive gifts from Him and also that we will be like Him.

To have an inheritance with Jesus—who is God—we must be His children. And to become His children, He must wash us in the waters of Baptism. It is in this Sacrament that Jesus cleanses us of Original Sin (which we all inherit from our first parents, Adam and Eve) and makes us adopted children of the Father. Now our inheritance is Heaven! Baptism washes away sin, gives us a new life in the Holy Spirit, and makes us members of the Body of Christ, the Church.

Death and rebirth

We are all born into life, but that life is in a broken relationship with God because of Original Sin. Adam and Eve's sin was not merely a personal one. This sin wounded human nature, making us weak and inclined to sin. That life must end before we can be

born again to a new life. St. Paul said, "You were buried with him in baptism, in which you were also raised with him through faith in the power of God, who raised him from the dead" (Colossians 2:12). Baptism is truly "the sacrament of regeneration through water in the word" (CCC 1213). Baptism allows us to share in Christ's Death for us on the Cross and His rising to new life. It "conforms" us to Christ by allowing us to participate in a small way in the things He did for us.

Symbols of Baptism

Each symbol of Baptism represents a different invisible truth happening within the celebration of the Sacrament. By recognizing these symbols and participating in the words and actions of the Sacrament, the newly baptized person is introduced to the many blessings of the Christian life.

The **Sign of the Cross** is made on the person to be baptized. This begins the celebration of the Sacrament and signifies the grace of redemption won for us by Christ on the Cross. The person is **anointed with the oil** of catechumens as a renunciation, or denial, of Satan and sin.

The person to be baptized must make a profession of faith, or in the case of infant Baptism, the parents make a profession of faith for their child. The words spoken in this profession of faith confess belief in the most important teachings of the Catholic Faith that will be entrusted to the person in Baptism.

The **baptismal water** is blessed by a priest, who asks the Holy Spirit to come upon the water so that the baptized may be "born of water and the spirit," as Jesus commanded.

At the moment of Baptism, the person is immersed in holy water, or holy water is poured on his head three times while the minister uses the same words Jesus commanded the Apostles to use when baptizing: **"I baptize you in the name of the Father, and of the Son, and of the Holy Spirit."** The triple immersion or pouring represents the newly baptized person's entry in the life of the Trinity.

After Baptism, the person is anointed with **sacred chrism or holy oil**. This anointing incorporates the person into Christ, who is Priest, Prophet, and King. In other words, the baptized "puts on Christ," and shares in Jesus' priestly, prophetic, and kingly roles. (This is the same oil that will be used to anoint in the Sacrament of Confirmation.)

The baptized person is given a **white garment** that signifies that he has "put on Christ" and has been washed clean of the stain of sin. The baptized person is also given a **candle** lit from the Easter candle. This symbolizes that Christ has enlightened his life so that he might be "the light of the world." Baptism makes an indelible (or permanent) mark on our soul. Therefore, it can be received only once. The baptized person receives sanctifying grace, which is God's life in us.

All your sins are forgiven through Baptism, including Original Sin. Your relationship with God that was broken by Original Sin is restored, and you become the adopted child of the Father: you can now call Him Father just as Jesus does, and your inheritance is Heaven! Now that Heaven is open to you, your task is to reach it.

1. What are two ways to understand the word inheritance?

   To pass down something from someone or to recevie a gift from them

2. Explain why St. Paul said, "You were buried with him in baptism, in which you were also raised with him through faith in the power of God, who raised him from the dead" (Colossians 2:12).

   So we can go through what christ went through for us washed
   our sins

3. List at least three symbols of Baptism and write their meanings.

   The sign of the cross, The holy oil , and baptisimal water
   a white garenet, Candle

4. Would you say that Baptism gives us a new inheritance, or does it restore our true inheritance? Explain.

It gives us an inheritance because none of us are sons\daughers of god (except Jesus). So we need to be given the inheritance so we can become the sons and daughters of the lord and so we can also be like him

St. Thomas Aquinas on the Sacraments

Directions: Read and reflect on the quotation below, then respond to the questions.

"A Sacrament is a sign that commemorates what precedes it – Christ's Passion; demonstrates what is accomplished in us through Christ's Passion – grace; and prefigures what that Passion pledges to us – future glory."

–ST. THOMAS AQUINAS

Define the following terms:

1. Sign _____

2. Commemorates _____

3. Precede _____

4. Passion _____

5. Grace _____

6. Prefigure _____

7. Pledge _____

8. Glory _____

Reflection Question

Think about what you already know about the Sacraments in general, and about Baptism specifically. What connections can you make with the St. Thomas Aquinas quote?

_____

_____

_____

_____

Baptism Prefigured

Directions: Read the information and the given Scripture passages and respond to the questions in the boxes on the chart.

God prefigured the Sacrament of Baptism throughout His saving work in Salvation History. From the very beginning, when the Spirit of God hovered over the primordial waters, to Noah and the Great Flood, to the crossing of the Red Sea and the River Jordan, we have always understood these events as the signs that point the way to Baptism. God's people pass from chaos, death, slavery, and sin, through powerful and life-giving waters, to new life in grace and freedom as a new creation.

Passage	How is the water connected to life or death?	What connection can you make to Baptism?
1 Genesis 1:1-3 life	water is present in creation and creation equals life	you become a new creation in life.
2 Genesis 7:11-23 Death		origanal sin is washed away in baptism
3 Exodus 2:1-10 life	moses is saved from death by floating in the water	we are saved from death and sin by the waters of baptisim
4 Exodus 7:20-24 Death		The blood of christ saves us from sin. when baptisim happens
5 Exodus 14:23-30 Death + Life	The hebrews make it and start a new life and the egyptians die	we start a new life when we are baptisted
6 Exodus 17:1-7 Life		
7 Joshua 3:14-17 Life	The waters part and Joshua is lead to the Promise land	we enter into heaven when we are baptist-ed

The Baptism of Jesus

Directions: Read the information below, then answer the questions that follow.

"After all the people had been baptized and Jesus also had been baptized and was praying, heaven was opened

and the holy Spirit descended upon him in bodily form like a dove. And a voice came from heaven, 'You are my beloved Son; with you I am well pleased.'"

–LUKE 3:21-22

Jesus, who had no sin, was baptized. Why would He have been baptized? Before He began His public ministry, Jesus allowed Himself to be baptized to give us a model of holiness. Before He ascended into Heaven, He commanded the Apostles to baptize people "in the name of the Father, and of the Son, and of the Holy Spirit."

For over 2,000 years, Christians have ministered this Sacrament. Today, parents usually ask their priest or deacon to baptize their baby. The parents promise to raise their child as a Christian, teaching him or her to live in obedience to God's commandments. They choose godparents to help them do this.

Then the priest pours water three times over the baby while saying the words Jesus commanded his Apostles to use, invoking the names of the Three Persons of the Blessed Trinity. The baby's white garment symbolizes purity and new life, and a candle is a sign of the light of Christ, which now shines invisibly in the baby's soul.

The Baptism of Christ, by Francesco Trevisani.

This is the visible part of Baptism, but the invisible reality is much greater. The Gospel account of Jesus' Baptism offers an insight. When Jesus was baptized, the Holy Spirit descended upon Him and the voice of God the Father spoke: "This is my beloved Son, in whom I am well pleased."

This is exactly what happens to every person being baptized. The Holy Spirit descends upon you, and the Father calls you His beloved child! You are adopted into the life of the Blessed Trinity. What Jesus has by nature, you now have by adoption. After Baptism, God the Father calls us "beloved son" or "beloved daughter" because we now participate in Jesus' sonship with the Father. Baptism sets us on the path to become Godlike by being conformed to Jesus.

The Holy Spirit now dwells within you. Heaven is open to you, love has been placed in your heart, and you can begin the process of growing in goodness and holiness.

1. What do you find most interesting about the account of Jesus' Baptism?

    _____

    _____

2. Does the painting look the way you had pictured this event in your mind? Why or why not?

    _____

    _____

    _____

3. A Sacrament is an outward, visible sign of an inward, invisible reality. How does that definition apply to what we read in the Gospels about Jesus' Baptism?

    _____

    _____

    _____

The Need for and Effects of Baptism

Directions: Read the essay and then answer the focus and reflection questions.

As the Lord made known to us, Baptism is necessary. But God's great mercy makes salvation possible for people who have not received the Sacrament. The *Catechism* teaches that "*God has bound salvation to the sacrament of Baptism, but he himself is not bound by his sacraments*" (1257). This means that the fruits of Baptism can be assured to some who have not received the Sacrament. A catechumen who dies before receiving Baptism, for example, is assured salvation through his or her desire for Baptism, repentance for sin, and charity. This is known as baptism of desire. An unbaptized person who dies for his or her faith in Jesus is baptized "by [his] death for and with Christ" (CCC 1258). This is called baptism of blood, and it brings about the effects of baptism without being a Sacrament. Third, someone who has never heard of Jesus and the Church but who seeks God and tries to do His will may be saved, because this person would have desired Baptism if he knew of it. Last, even though there is no definite teaching, we have hope that children who die without having been baptized will somehow be saved. Jesus said, "Let the children come to me; do not prevent them" (Mark 10:14), which allows us to have this hope.

The Church takes her mission of the salvation of all souls very seriously. The Church's main mission is to invite all people everywhere to hear the Good News of the Gospel and be baptized. God established Baptism as the

Tapestry showing the Baptism of Constantine, workshop of Philippe Maëcht and Hans Taye

normal means of salvation from sin. For those who have been introduced to God and His Church and know what His will is for our lives, there is no other sure path to Heaven.

The effects of Baptism

Our first pope proclaimed the importance of Baptism: "Peter [said] to them, 'Repent and be baptized, every one of you, in the name of Jesus Christ for the forgiveness of your sins; and you will receive the gift of the holy Spirit'" (Acts 2:38). Forgiveness of sins and receiving the gift of the Holy Spirit are the two main effects of Baptism. There are others that we recognize. Baptism makes us a new creation as an adopted child of the Father; it makes us a member of the Church; it forms bonds of Christian unity; and it imprints an indelible mark on our souls.

Baptism forgives sin

The Sacrament of Baptism forgives all sin, including Original Sin, and any punishment for sin.

All sins have spiritual consequences, most especially mortal sin, which separates us from God. Baptism forgives all of these sins and removes all spiritual consequences. At the moment of Baptism, there is nothing that would prevent the baptized from entering Heaven.

Baptism forgives sin, but it doesn't remove sin or its effects from the world. Some earthly consequences for sin remain after Baptism, including suffering, sickness, and death during our earthly lives. Also, all of humanity experiences a tendency to sin called concupiscence. But we can resist this human weakness with the help of God's grace.

Baptism makes you a new creation

The Sacrament of Baptism makes the baptized a new creation in the eyes of God: His adopted sons and daughters and sharers in His divine life. A child inherits what is the parent's. As children of the Father, we become inheritors of all God's promises, and our bodies become temples of the Holy Spirit. This is all possible because Baptism gives us sanctifying grace. Sanctifying grace is the undeserved gift of God's life within us. It makes us able to believe in God, to hope in His promises of salvation, and to love Him and all that He has made. Sanctifying grace also gives us the power to live a holy life with the help of the Holy Spirit. This is why Baptism is the foundation of the Christian life. It is also why, since the earliest days of the Church, children and babies have been baptized. The graces we receive, which do not come from anything we have done to merit them, are the gateway to true freedom.

Baptism makes you a member of the Church

The Sacrament of Baptism makes the baptized a member of the Church, the Body of Christ. We become united to everyone who has also been baptized. Together we become one people of God. Scripture explains that Baptism makes us "a chosen race, a royal priesthood, a holy nation, a people of [God's] own" (1 Peter 2:9). This means that the baptized are made into a common priesthood of all believers, who are called to serve one another in love and sacrifice. As members of Christ's Church, we are given all the rights and privileges that come with membership. This means that we are set apart and made ready for Christian worship, we may go on to receive all the other Sacraments, and we receive all the other spiritual help of the Church. The baptized also are given the mission of the Church, which is to share the Good News of Jesus Christ with all who will hear it. The baptized who profess the Faith of the Church must also be obedient to the teachings and leaders of the Church, who were appointed by Jesus Himself.

Baptism imprints an indelible mark on your soul

The Sacrament of Baptism gives the baptized an indelible, or permanent, spiritual mark on his or her soul. This spiritual mark is not removable, even if the baptized person sins or gives up his Faith. Therefore, the Sacrament of Baptism can be received only once. The Holy Spirit places this mark upon our souls to set us apart for the day of redemption. Over the course of our lives, this indelible mark enables us to participate in the Mass. It also allows us to use the gifts of the Holy Spirit given to us at our Baptism to live lives of holiness. The Christian who remains faithful to the demands of his or her Baptism will leave this life "marked with the sign of faith" (CCC 1274) and expect to enter the Kingdom of God and be saved.

Baptism forges bonds of Christian unity

The Sacrament of Baptism goes beyond any barriers we may perceive based on race, nationality, culture, or sex and makes us one Body of Christ. Other Christian faiths also celebrate Baptism. We recognize the truth of proper Baptism that occurs outside of the Catholic Church. Therefore, Baptism makes us all brothers and sisters in Christ and rightly called Christians. Although some Protestants do not believe in the effects of Baptism, Baptism indeed forms a sacramental bond of unity among everyone who is reborn through it.

Define the following terms:

1. Baptism of desire: _is when a adult wants to be baptisted this is the kind they get_

2. Baptism of blood: _is when a unbaptisted person dies for god and faith. In this way they are baptisted by their death_

3. What is the main mission of the Church?

   Their mission is to invite all people to hear the good news of the gosple and baptisim. So to save souls; basicly

4. What is sanctifying grace?

   _____

Reflection Question

How would you assess the importance of Baptism? Explain on your own paper in a well-reasoned essay.

Baptism Graphic Organizer

Directions: Use the information you have read, your class notes, and the *Catechism of the Catholic Church* nos. 1212-1284 to complete 1-5 on this chart. Share your personal reflections for 6-7.

1	Scriptural basis of this Sacrament.	Jesus is baptisim and Jesus damands that his paople baptise believers in the father, Son, holy spirit
2	Words spoken with this Sacrament (form).	I baptise you in the name of the father Son and holy spirit
3	Things used or done when this Sacrament is received (matter).	The things done are the triple evertion orf pouring of water, lighting a candle and being Presented in a white garnet, and anointing of oil.
4	Effects of this Sacrament.	it washes away origanal + all sin, you come to be a new creation, you becoming a member of the church, you get this permanent mark on your soul
5	Ordinary minister of this Sacrament.	any one can baptise anyone as long as they hold the intent of the church
6	How does this Sacrament reveal God's life-giving love?	
7	How does this Sacrament help you to become more like your Heavenly Father?	

Sophia SketchPad Reflection Questions

Directions: Answer the questions below after watching and discussing the video.

1. Did you gain any new insights about the Sacrament of Baptism after watching this video? If so, what were they? If not, which part of the video did you think provided the clearest or most interesting information? Explain.

   _____

   _____

   _____

   _____

   _____

2. On your own paper, draw your own sketch explaining in greater detail one of the effects of Baptism.

Confirmation Pre-Assessment

Directions: In the left-hand column mark each statement true or false. Mark them again in the right-hand column at the end of our study of Confirmation to see if you were right.

Before beginning your study

At the end of your study

True or False?   **Statement**   **True or False?**

False ___ 1. Confirmation is like your "graduation" from religious education because it makes you an "adult" in the religious community.   _____

_____ 2. As soon as Jesus rose from the dead on Easter Sunday, the Apostles had the fortitude to tell the world about Him.   _____

_____ 3. You receive the Sacrament of Confirmation to show the world that you are ready to claim the Catholic Faith as your own.   _____

False ___ 4. Confirmation gives you the gifts of the Holy Spirit: wisdom, understanding, counsel, fortitude, knowledge, piety, and fear of the Lord.   _____

True ___ 5. Although much has changed, today's world has a lot in common with the one the Apostles lived in.   _____

False ___ 6. When you are confirmed, you should expect to feel different right away.   _____

True ___ 7. Pentecost is considered the "birthday of the Church."   _____

True ___ 8. The Church offers Confirmation to those who would like to receive it, but it is not truly necessary to the Christian life.   _____

A Promise and a Command

Directions: Read the verse from the Book of the Acts of the Apostles. Then answer the questions that follow.

"But you will receive power when the holy Spirit comes upon you, and you will be my witnesses in Jerusalem, throughout Judea and Samaria, and to the ends of the earth. "

–ACTS 1:8

1. Who is speaking in this verse? _____

2. To whom is He speaking? _____

3. What promise does He make? _____

_____

4. What responsibility comes with this promise?

_____

_____

_____

5. What does it mean to be a witness?

_____

_____

_____

The Story of Confirmation

Directions: Read the essay, then answer the questions that follow.

God has always desired for His people to be a "royal priesthood," anointed and consecrated as His Chosen People. The Sacrament of Confirmation completes the work begun in us at our Baptism and sets us apart as this very royal priesthood proclaimed since the Old Testament. We receive an outpouring of the Holy Spirit in Confirmation that empowers us, like the Apostles at Pentecost, to proclaim the Good News of Jesus Christ and make disciples of all the nations.

Confirmation perfects your baptismal grace

When you are baptized, you are reborn in the Holy Spirit. When you are confirmed, the grace you received at Baptism is made stronger, and you are united more closely with Jesus and the Church. The gifts of the Holy Spirit grow greater in you, and you are given a special strength to spread and protect our Faith. While Baptism is the "doorway" to Christian life, Confirmation helps give us the strength to carry on in that life.

Like all the Sacraments, Confirmation has roots in the Bible. The story of Pentecost in chapter 2 of Acts is the main biblical foundation of Confirmation.

At Pentecost, thousands of Jews had gathered from many regions. Mary and the Apostles were gathered together in the Upper Room. Then, suddenly: "There came from the sky a noise like a strong driving wind, and it filled the entire house in which they were. Then there appeared to them tongues as of fire, which parted and came to rest on each one of them. And they were all filled with the holy Spirit and began to speak in different tongues, as the Spirit enabled them to proclaim" (Acts 2:2-4). Jesus had kept His promise that He would send His Holy Spirit.

The Virgin Mary and the Apostles received an outpouring of grace that strengthened them to share the Gospel. As the numbers of disciples grew, others were called to preach the Gospel message. "They presented these men to the apostles who prayed and laid hands on them" (Acts 6:6). The Apostles became ministers of this Sacrament, to give this gift of the Holy Spirit, in turn, to the faithful. This is what happens when you are confirmed.

The Rite of Confirmation

The laying on of hands was a traditional Jewish way of selecting someone for a task and asking for God's blessing on that person to carry it out. That tradition is recognized by the Church as the origin of the Sacrament of Confirmation.

Early in Church history, anointing with oil was added to the rite of Confirmation to signify the gift of the Holy Spirit. When you are confirmed, the bishop lays his hands on you and anoints you with oil in the same way the Apostles laid hands on the faithful of their day. You are taking part in a mystery that links us to the past and links us directly to

Jesus: the Person who lived on earth and our Lord in Heaven.

In Baptism, Christ cleanses us like – and with – water. In Confirmation, He anoints us like – and with – oil. Oil cleanses, soothes, strengthens, and beautifies us. The anointing is a seal and a consecration. Jesus said, "For on [the Son of Man] the Father, God, has set his seal" (John 6:27b). Just as the Son of God was sealed by the Father, we are sealed to the Father in Confirmation. Jesus often called His Father – and our Father – Abba. This is the closest word in Aramaic for "Father." Confirmation, through God's grace, roots us more deeply into this love.

Jesus promised the gift of the Holy Spirit, which was received by the Apostles at Pentecost. From there, the Apostles followed Jesus' command to make disciples of all the nations by baptizing them, and they bestowed upon them what they had received – the gift of the Holy Spirit – so that these new disciples could do as the Apostles did and proclaim Jesus as Lord.

And so it makes sense that a candidate for Confirmation who has reached the age of reason must believe in Jesus, intend to receive the Sacrament, and be prepared to take on the role of disciple and witness to Christ in the Church and the world. A candidate for Confirmation must also be in a state of grace. It is important to receive the Sacrament of Penance and Reconciliation regularly, and it is necessary before being confirmed if a candidate has un-confessed mortal sin.

1. How are the Sacraments of Baptism and Confirmation connected to each other?
   In baptisim we receive many things including a strong relationship with god. In Conformation These gifts and bond are strengthed

2. In Confirmation, what are we strengthened with the gifts of the Holy Spirit to do?
   To be set apart for spefic tasks

3. What happened at Pentecost? the sky opened and the holy spirit came

4. What did the Virgin Mary and the Apostles receive at Pentecost? the strength to share the gosple

5. What did the laying on of hands traditionally represent for the Jewish people?
   It represents the task that some will do and carry out

6. Why was anointing with oil added to the Sacrament of Confirmation early in the history of the Church?
   To signify the holy spirit

7. What do we become linked to when we receive the Sacrament of Confirmation? How does this Sacrament help us become more like Christ?

_____

_____

8. Why does Christ anoint us with oil in the Sacrament of Confirmation?

because it seals what we have done in baptisim and conformation

Reflection Questions

9. What does it mean to be "set apart" for something? How does it feel to be set apart? How does our being set apart show us how much God loves us?

_____

_____

_____

_____

10. How does Confirmation reveal God's life-giving love?

_____

_____

_____

11. In the East, Christians receive the Sacrament of Confirmation immediately after Baptism. They then begin receiving the Eucharist right away. This tradition highlights the unity of the three sacraments of Christian initiation: Baptism, Confirmation, and Eucharist. Which tradition do you prefer, and why?

_____

_____

_____

_____

_____

_____

_____

Confirmation Prefigured

Directions: Read the given Scripture passages and respond to the questions in the boxes on the chart. Then answer the reflection question.

	How is the Spirit of God present in the passage?	What does the Spirit give the person or empower him to do?
1 Genesis 2:7		
2 1 Samuel 16:13		
3 Ezekiel 36:26-27		
4 Joel 3:1-2		

	How is the Spirit of God present in the passage?	What does the Spirit give the person or empower him to do?
5 Isaiah 11:2		
6 Isaiah 61:1		

Reflection Question

Choose your favorite verse from the chart and apply it to your own life. Whether or not you have been confirmed, how can you be more open to the promptings of the Holy Spirit?

_____

_____

_____

_____

_____

_____

_____

Pentecostés

BY FRAY JUAN BAUTIST A MAINO (C. 1615-1620)

Museo del Prado, Madrid.

Pentecostés

Pentecostés, by Friar Juan Bautista Maíno (c. 1615-1620)

Directions: Take some time to quietly view and reflect on the art. Let yourself be inspired in any way that happens naturally. Then think about the questions below, and discuss them with your classmates.

Discussion Questions

1. What moment from the Bible does this painting depict?

2. What is your favorite part?

3. How does the artist's use of color affect the way you respond to the painting?

4. Where is the light coming from in the scene?

5. What are the symbols of the Holy Spirit?

6. What symbols of the Holy Spirit do you see in the artwork?

7. Read Acts 2:1-4 below. How does this painting help you understand this Gospel passage?

> When the time for Pentecost was fulfilled, they were all in one place together. And suddenly there came from the sky a noise like a strong driving wind, and it filled the entire house in which they were. Then there appeared to them tongues as of fire, which parted and came to rest on each one of them. And they were all filled with the Holy Spirit and began to speak in different tongues, as the Spirit enabled them to proclaim.

8. Write at least two sentences linking the people in this painting or the Sacrament of Confirmation to one or more people in the Old Testament. For example, *God breathed new life into the Apostles at Pentecost, as He breathed life into Adam.*

9. How would you connect this painting and the Sacrament of Confirmation to our first pope's words in 1 Peter 2:9:

> But you are "a chosen race, a royal priesthood, a holy nation, a people of his own, so that you may announce the praises" of him who called you out of darkness into his wonderful light.

The Effects of Confirmation

Directions: Read the essay and then answer the focus and reflection questions.

Jesus promised the gift of the Holy Spirit, which was received by the Apostles at Pentecost. From there, the Apostles followed Jesus' command to make disciples of all the nations by baptizing them, and they bestowed upon them what they had received, the gift of the Holy Spirit, so that these new disciples could do as the Apostles did and proclaim Jesus as Lord.

"Be sealed with the gift of the Holy Spirit." These are the words spoken by the bishop as he anoints the forehead of the confirmand (the person being confirmed) with holy oil. The holy oil, called chrism in the Latin Rite, and myron in Eastern Rites, is a visible symbol of the seal of the Holy Spirit. The oil that is used in Confirmation is the same oil that is used to anoint the newly baptized as priest, prophet, and king.

Indeed, there is a close connection between the Sacraments of Baptism and Confirmation. This connection is found not only in the oil and the outpouring of the Holy Spirit received in both Sacraments, but also in the symbols used to show forth those graces.

In ancient times, anointing with oil had many meanings. The oil was often perfumed and smelled sweet and pleasing. It was a sign of being clean, and often people would anoint themselves after bathing. It was a sign of healing and was used to soothe wounds. Athletes would use oil to loosen up stiff joints and muscles. Anointing with oil was a symbol of abundance, joy, beauty, good health, and strength.

Anointing with oil was also a sign of consecration, or of being set apart or sealed as belonging to another. This is what is meant when the bishop says "Be sealed..." A seal is a symbol of belonging. A soldier bore his leader's seal into battle. A personal letter would be marked with the author's seal to ensure that it was authentic. Jesus – the authentic Messiah – proclaimed that He was marked with His Father's seal, which He then gave us as a share in His mission as priest, prophet, and king.

In the Sacraments, anointing with oil shares these same meanings. Anointing at Baptism symbolizes cleansing, while Anointing of the Sick symbolizes healing. Anointing at Confirmation is a sign of strengthening. It symbolizes an abundant outpouring of the Holy Spirit, and the beauty and joy of the fullness of the Christian life. Anointing at Confirmation also symbolizes being consecrated to God. By the Sacrament of Confirmation we are sealed with God's Spirit and set apart as belonging to Him. We bear His seal in the battle between good and evil waged all around us. The seal is an indelible mark on our soul – it can never be lost.

This understanding of anointing puts St. Paul's words in Ephesians 6:13-17 into sharper focus: "Therefore, put on the armor of God ... stand fast with your loins girded in truth, clothed with righteousness as a breastplate, and your feet shod in readiness for the gospel of peace. In all circumstances, hold faith as a shield, to quench all [the] flaming arrows of the evil one. And take the helmet of salvation and the sword of the Spirit, which is the word of God." By the Sacrament of Confirmation we are equipped with the sword and shield of faith and the Holy Spirit to fight the good fight and proclaim the Good News of Jesus Christ to all.

Another symbol of the gift of the Holy Spirit is the laying on of hands. In the Sacrament of Confirmation, the bishop lays his hands on the confirmand as a sign of the bestowing of the Spirit that he himself received in the very same way. The laying on of hands is a powerful symbol of an unbroken line of grace that extends back to Jesus and the Apostles.

The effects of the Sacrament

You were given seeds of grace at your Baptism, and Confirmation strengthens and perfects that grace. The Sacrament of Confirmation more perfectly binds a baptized person to the Church and fills him or her with a special strength of the Holy Spirit. The *Catechism of the Catholic Church* teaches, "The effect of the sacrament of Confirmation is the special outpouring of the Holy Spirit as once granted to the apostles on the day of Pentecost. From this fact, Confirmation brings an increase and deepening of baptismal grace: it roots us more deeply in the divine filiation which makes us cry 'Abba! Father!' [Filiation refers to the relationship of a son or daughter to his or her parents.] It unites us more firmly to Christ. It renders

[or makes] our bond with the Church more perfect" (adapted from CCC 1302-1303).

At Confirmation you also receive the Gifts of the Holy Spirit. Since grace perfects nature, these gifts build on your natural virtues. The Gifts of the Holy Spirit are wisdom, counsel, understanding, fortitude, knowledge, piety, and fear of the Lord. (You may have heard of courage as a Gift of the Holy Spirit. But *courage* and *fortitude* are not quite synonyms. Fortitude is a stronger virtue than courage.)

St. Peter is a good example of someone whose natural virtue was strengthened by grace. St. Peter had the natural fortitude to follow Jesus, but he needed spiritual fortitude in order to preach. He received a special outpouring of grace at Pentecost, the scriptural foundation of Confirmation, and only then was he able to come out of hiding and boldly preach the Gospel.

But the Gifts of the Holy Spirit do not instantly transform you. You must choose to accept these gifts and nurture them as you would a seed. You were created with free will, and that means that for the graces to become more meaningful and effective—for those seeds to bear fruit—you must freely choose to nurture and develop them. You can do this by spending time with God in prayer, going to Mass and Confession regularly, and striving to live a virtuous life. Virtues help us avoid sin. The goal of a virtuous life is to become like God—to participate in His divine life of love here on earth and to get to Heaven.

1. What does the bishop say during the Sacrament of Confirmation?

   Be sealed with the gift of the holy Spirit

2. Why is there a close connection between Baptism and Confirmation?

   The oil, The Symbols, and the outpouring of the holy spirit It perfects the gifts of baptisim

3. What does it mean to be consecrated? _To be set apart from others_

4. What is an example of a seal? _a soldier bore his leader's seal into battle_

5. How is anointing with oil in the Sacrament of Confirmation similar to the different meanings of being anointed in ancient times?

They symbolize similar things

6. How does St. Paul's description of the armor of God in Ephesians 6 help you better understand the Sacrament of Confirmation? _+ holy spirit_

we are equipt with the sword and shield of faith to fight the good fight and proclaim the good news of the church + gosple

7. What does the laying on of hands symbolize? _bestowing of the holy spirit_

8. What are the gifts of the Holy Spirit?

wisdom, counsel, understanding, fortitude, knowledge, piety, and fear of the lord

9. What is the goal of a virtuous life? _by nuturing the gifts of these sacraments_

Reflection Questions

10. Why do you think a bishop (and not a priest) is the ordinary minister of this Sacrament?

_____

_____

11. After you are confirmed, you bear Jesus' seal in the battle between good and evil waged all around you. How will you contribute to this battle?

_____

_____

12. Now that you have learned more about this Sacrament, how does it help you to become more like your Heavenly Father?

_____

_____

Gifts of the Holy Spirit

Directions: Read about each gift of the Holy Spirit, then look up and write out the Scripture verse. Finally, respond to the question that follows each gift.

Fortitude

A steady will to do good, in spite of difficulties. Fortitude is a gift of the Holy Spirit and a cardinal virtue.

JOHN 16:33: _____

_____

_____

1. Why do you think Jesus tells us to "take heart"? What does the heart have to do with fortitude?

_____

_____

Wisdom

Helps us respond to God as we contemplate (think about and meditate on) divine things. Wisdom is a gift of the Holy Spirit.

PROVERBS 3:18: _____

_____

2. The sacred author uses a metaphor to tell us that wisdom is a "tree of life." How is wisdom like a tree? How does it give us life?

_____

_____

Understanding

Helps us grasp revealed truths more easily. Understanding is a gift of the Holy Spirit.

MATTHEW 10:19-20: _____

_____

_____

3. What are some things you can do to hear God speaking to you more clearly?

_____

_____

Counsel

Helps us judge quickly and correctly. Counsel is a gift of the Holy Spirit.

PROVERBS 3:1: _____

_____

_____

4. To whom do you usually go for advice? Does anyone ever ask you for your advice? How do you know what to tell them?

_____

_____

Knowledge

Awareness of God's plan for our lives. Knowledge is a gift of the Holy Spirit.

2 PETER 1:5: _____

_____

_____

5. When you know something, how do you know that you know it?

_____

_____

Piety

Loyalty to God and divine things. Piety is a gift of the Holy Spirit.

ROMANS 8:16: _____

_____

_____

6. Would someone who doesn't know you be able to tell you are a Christian from observing the way you treat others? Explain.

_____

_____

Fear of the Lord

Deep respect for God that helps us avoid sin. Fear of the Lord is a gift of the Holy Spirit.

PSALM 119:120: _____

_____

_____

7. Fear of the Lord is sometimes called "awe." What does *awe* mean? Have you ever seen anything or been anywhere that made you feel awe?

_____

_____

Confirmation Graphic Organizer

Directions: Use information from this guide, your class notes, and the *Catechism of the Catholic Church* nos. 1285-1321 to complete 1-5 on this chart. Share your personal reflections for 6-7.

1 Scriptural basis of this Sacrament.	
2 Words spoken with this Sacrament (form).	
3 Things used or done when this Sacrament is received (matter).	
4 Effects of this Sacrament.	
5 Ordinary minister of this Sacrament.	
6 How does this Sacrament reveal God's life-giving love?	
7 How does this Sacrament help you to become more like your Heavenly Father?	

Sophia SketchPad Reflection Questions

Directions: Answer the questions below after watching and discussing the video.

1. Did you gain any new insights about the Sacrament of Confirmation after watching this
    video? If so, what were they? If not, which part of the video did you think provided the
    clearest or most interesting information? Explain.

    _____

    _____

    _____

2. In your own life – in your family, your school, your community – you will come across people
    who are in need of conversion and repentance, just as the Apostles did. What are some ways
    you can charitably share the Gospel, not just in your words, but in the way you live and act
    on a daily basis?

    _____

    _____

    _____

Young Saints

Directions: Select one of the saints below and look up his or her life story. Then answer the questions below.

- St. Dominic Savio
- Bl. Pier Giorgio Frassati
- St. Bernadette
- St. Thérèse of Lisieux
- St. Gemma Galgani

- St. Kateri Tekakwitha
- St. Philomena
- Bl. Jacinta and Francesco Marto
- St. Lucy

1. How was the saint you selected strengthened by the Holy Spirit to serve God and others? Explain.

_____

_____

_____

_____

2. What can you learn from your saint's life as an example to "not be afraid" in your own life?

_____

_____

_____

_____

Eucharist Pre-Assessment

Directions: In the left-hand column mark each statement true or false. Mark them again in the right-hand column at the end of our study of the Eucharist to see if you were right.

Before beginning your study

At the end of your study

True or False?   **Statement**   **True or False?**

_____   1. Jesus instituted the Sacrament of the Eucharist at the Last Supper.   _____

_____   2. Jesus' teaching on the Bread of Life can be found in the Letter to the Corinthians.   _____

_____   3. You must receive the Eucharist at least once before you turn 18, and at least once more thereafter.   _____

_____   4. The Eucharist is the Body and Blood of Jesus Christ.   _____

_____   5. In addition to receiving the Eucharist at Holy Mass, we can be with Jesus in Eucharistic Adoration.   _____

_____   6. The Eucharist is the memorial of Christ's Passover.   _____

_____   7. The Eucharist unites us more closely to Jesus.   _____

_____   8. The Church offers the Eucharist to those who would like to receive it, but it is not truly necessary to the Christian life.   _____

Adoration of the Lamb
BY MICHIEL COXIE (C. 1557-1559)

Bode-Museum, Berlin.

Adoration of the Lamb

Adoration of the Lamb, by Michiel Coxie (c. 1557-1559)

Directions: Take some time to quietly view and reflect on the art. Let yourself be inspired in any way that happens naturally. Then think about the questions below, and discuss them with your classmates.

Discussion Questions

1. What do you see happening in this painting?
   I see people worshiping lamb

2. What is on the altar? Whom or what does it symbolize? What is catching its blood?
   a lamb   *the altar*

3. What do you see above the altar? Whom or what does it symbolize?
   a dove   *the holy spirit*

4. Jesus' cousin John the Baptist said about Jesus, "Behold the Lamb of God who takes away the sin of the world." Why did John call Jesus a Lamb?
   because the lamb sybolizes Jesus

5. Recall the story of the Exodus, when Moses led the Israelites out of slavery in Egypt. What did God tell the Israelites to do on the night that the Angel of Death passed through Egypt?
   take a perfect eatit and put its blood on their doorstep

6. Jesus instituted a New Passover. What would be the sacrifice for this New Covenant?

7. The angels behind the altar are holding a cross with a crown of leaves, a spear, a scourge and a sponge, a column and a rod. What might be the significance of these things?

8. What did the Israelites do with the Passover lamb? (Hint: See Exodus 12:8.)
   they ate it

What Is the Eucharist?

Directions: Read the information, then answer the questions that follow.

The Eucharist is the Body and Blood of Jesus Christ. It is not just a symbol or a sign but His real Body and Blood. The change of the bread and wine into the Body and Blood of Jesus is called Transubstantiation. The entire substance of the bread and wine changes, although they appear the same as they did before the change. Validly ordained priests have the power to invoke the Holy Spirit and pronounce the words of consecration when they act in the person of Christ through the power of the Sacrament of Holy Orders. "By the consecration the transubstantiation of the bread and wine into the Body and Blood of Christ is brought about. Under the consecrated species of bread and wine Christ himself, living and glorious, is present in a true, real, and substantial manner: his Body and his Blood, with his soul and his divinity" (CCC 1413).

The bread and wine are not symbols of Jesus' Body. *The Baltimore Catechism* explains one of the ways we know this: "Christ could not have used clearer, more explicit words than

'This is My body.' He did not say, 'This is a sign of My body' or 'This represents My body,' but, 'This is My body.' Catholics take Christ at His word because He is the omnipotent God. On His word they know that the Holy Eucharist is the body and blood of Christ."

What Are Its Fruits?

When we receive Holy Communion, we grow closer to Christ. The Eucharist helps us avoid sin and strengthens our charity. It helps us to see the face of Jesus in the poor.

The *Catechism* explains, "Participation in the Holy Sacrifice identifies us with [Jesus'] Heart, sustains our strength along the pilgrimage of this life, makes us long for eternal life, and unites us even now to the Church in heaven, the Blessed Virgin Mary, and all the saints" (CCC 1419).

We will learn much more about the effects of the Eucharist, as well as how we should receive it, in the coming days.

1. What is the Eucharist? The body and blood Soul and divinity of Christ

2. How do we know it is the Body and Blood of Jesus?
   because Jesus said so

3. The Eucharist helps us to see the face of Jesus in the poor. Why would that be important?
   when you help the poor you are helping God\Jesus so should we

4. What is a *pilgrimage*? Why does the *Catechism* refer to our life on earth as a *pilgrimage*?

a journey to a place ~~place~~ _eucarist gives us food for our pilgrimage to heaven_

5. How does the Eucharist reveal God's self-giving love?

He gives hiself up for us

How Do We Receive the Body and Blood of Christ?

Directions: Read and discuss the information below with your parents, and discuss the questions that follow as a family.

How do we receive the Body of Christ?

You can receive the Eucharist on your tongue (the ordinary way), a traditional sign of our humility before God and an acknowledgment that it is Christ who feeds us. You may also receive Communion in your hands (the optional way). If you do so, you should make sure your hands are clean and empty, placing your left hand flat over your right, and that you put the host in your mouth right away rather than waiting until you return to your pew.

We should receive – never take – the Eucharist in a way that demonstrates the respect and awe we have for God. Some of the other ways we do this include:

> fasting for at least one hour before receiving Communion, except for water and medicine.

> dressing appropriately for Mass as a sign of respect.

> genuflecting toward the Real Presence of Jesus in the tabernacle before we enter a pew.

> focusing our minds and hearts on the mystery we are about to encounter.

> receiving reverently.

> kneeling in prayer when we return to our pew after receiving until the sacred

vessels have been purified; for example, you could pray the *Anima Christi*, a prayer from the 14th century:

Soul of Christ, sanctify me.
Body of Christ, save me.
Blood of Christ, inebriate me.
Water from the side of Christ, wash me.
Passion of Christ, strengthen me.
O good Jesus, hear me.
Within Thy wounds hide me.
Suffer me not to be separated from Thee.
From the malicious enemy defend me.
In the hour of my death call me.
And bid me come unto Thee
That I may praise Thee with Thy saints
and with Thy angels
Forever and ever.
Amen.

Who can receive Communion?

Non-Catholics and Catholics who are in a state of mortal sin may not receive Communion. This may cause some to feel excluded. So why does the Church insist on this rule? There are several good reasons.

Our culture emphasizes inclusion, which can be a good thing. But there are times when there are good reasons to exclude certain people. A first-year medical student should be excluded from operating on patients. This doesn't mean first-year medical students are bad people; it just means they don't belong in an operating room unsupervised. They don't understand yet how to use the tools of a surgeon. In the same way, not believing and practicing the Catholic Faith does not make someone a bad person, but it means that he or she should not receive the Eucharist. Anyone who isn't fully initiated into the life of the Church cannot receive the gifts the Eucharist offers.

When we receive the Eucharist, the priest says, "The Body of Christ," and we respond, "Amen," which means "so be it," or "I agree." For this reason, it would be a lie for non-Catholics and others who do not believe the Eucharist is the Lord to receive the Eucharist.

The *Catechism* and canon law provide for very limited circumstances in which, in case of "grave necessity," such as the danger of death, Sacraments may be administered to those who ask, "provided that they manifest Catholic faith … and are properly disposed" (CIC 844 § 4).

Catholics in a state of mortal sin also may not receive the Eucharist. When we receive the Eucharist – the Body and Blood of Jesus Christ – into our souls, our souls should be ready to give Him a good, pure home. Our souls should be in the state of grace to receive Him worthily. If we are in the state of mortal sin and receive the Eucharist, we commit sacrilege, treating a sacred object unworthily, as if we don't care. Sacrilege violates the first commandment. Confession restores grace to the soul and purifies the soul for the Eucharist.

Why should we receive Communion often?

Just as we need to eat and drink several times a day to maintain our physical strength, so we also need to receive the Eucharist to feed the soul. The very Body of Christ, the Eucharist, strengthens and nourishes the Body of Christ – the Church – whose members are gathered in the Eucharistic celebration. When we eat food, our bodies receive the nourishment they need to maintain strength. When we eat the Eucharist, our souls receive the nourishment they need to maintain strength.

Frequent reception of the Eucharist, explains the *Catechism*, increases charity in our daily life, and that charity allows us to root ourselves in Christ (CCC 1394). Frequent reception of the Eucharist helps us to reach our spiritual goals and to avoid those things that lead us to sin.

Catholics are required to receive Communion at least once a year, but the Church warmly invites us to receive it much more often: every week, even every day! We should not think of the Eucharist as just a "requirement" in any case. St. Jean Vianney said, "If we really understood the Mass, we would die of joy." The next time you go to Mass, recall the words of this saint and try to focus your mind on the awesome gift Jesus is offering you. You will find that the more you do this, the more you will look forward to the time you give to Jesus each week and allow Him to love you in the Eucharist.

Conversation Questions

1. What is the Eucharist? What are some ways we know it is not just a symbol?

2. Did anything in this reading surprise you?

3. Did anything in this reading give you ideas for how you can approach Jesus more reverently each time you go to Mass?

4. Did this reading spark any ideas for things you can do to grow closer to Christ?

5. How does the Eucharist reveal God's self-giving love?

The Eucharist Prefigured

Directions: St. Augustine said, "The New Testament lies hidden in the Old, and the Old Testament is unveiled in the New." Read each pair of Scripture passages and write a one-paragraph reflection on how this St. Augustine quote applies: How does each verse help us understand the other in new ways?

Verse Pair 1

Then the LORD said to Moses: "I am going to rain down bread from heaven for you." –EXODUS 16:4

I am the bread of life. Your ancestors ate the manna in the desert, but they died; this is the bread that comes down from heaven so that one may eat it and not die. I am the living bread that came down from heaven; whoever eats this bread will live forever; and the bread that I will give is my flesh for the life of the world. –JOHN 6:48–51

How does each verse help us understand the other in new ways?

_____

_____

Verse Pair 2

My cup overflows. Indeed, goodness and mercy will pursue me all the days of my life. –PSALM 23:5B–6

This cup is the new covenant in my blood, which will be shed for you. –LUKE 22:20B

How does each verse help us understand the other in new ways?

_____

_____

Verse Pair 3

Then [Moses] took the blood and splashed it on the people, saying, "This is the blood of the covenant which the LORD has made with you according to all these words." –EXODUS 24:8

He said to them, "This is my blood of the covenant, which will be shed for many."
-MARK 14:24

How does each verse help us understand the other in new ways?

_____

_____

Verse Pair 4

A day of the LORD is coming. ...[L]iving water will flow out from Jerusalem.
–ZECHARIAH 14:1, 8 (NIV)

[O]ne soldier thrust his lance into his side, and immediately blood and water flowed out.
-JOHN 19:34

How does each verse help us understand the other in new ways?

_____

_____

Transubstantiation

Directions: Read the essay and complete the focus and reflection questions.

At Mass, when the priest says the words of consecration, "This is my body which will be given up for you … this is the cup of my blood …," the bread and wine literally become the Body and Blood of our Lord, Jesus Christ. This is a difficult teaching to understand. The Eucharist still looks like bread and wine and when we receive it, it still tastes like bread and wine. But it is truly no longer bread and wine. It has become Jesus' Body and Blood, Soul and Divinity. How does this happen?

We can think about what is necessary for something to be what it is and not something else. For example, what makes a chair a chair rather than a table? A chair has certain necessary characteristics that make it a chair. It does not possess the characteristics to be a table. These necessary characteristics are called "substantial forms." The substantial form of a chair is its "chair-ness." In other words, the substantial form of a chair is what is necessary for a chair to be a chair and not a table, or a banana, or something else entirely. Normally, you cannot change the substantial form of something without changing that thing into something else completely. If you change the substantial form of a chair, it would no longer be a chair. You could take it apart and use the wood and nails to make something else. Then it would become a table, or a stool, or something else entirely.

We can also think about characteristics of something that do NOT make it what it is. For example, what a chair is made of does

Holy Mass: Heaven, Earth, Purgatory.

not make it a chair. A chair can be made of wood, or metal, or plastic, or many other types of material. A chair is also not a chair because of its color. A chair could be colored red, or blue, or green. What a chair is made of or what color it is doesn't make a chair what it is. These sorts of characteristics are called "accidents." The word "accident" simply means that even though the characteristic is a part of something, it does not make that something what it is. Color, for example, only makes a chair red, or blue, or green. It does not make a chair a chair, or something else instead. You can even change the accidents of a thing, and it will still be that thing. You can paint a red chair blue, or replace a wooden chair's legs with plastic, and it still remains a chair.

What does any of this have to do with the Eucharist? On one hand, it is enough just to know that by the power of the Holy Spirit, Jesus' Body and Blood, Soul and Divinity become truly present under the appearances of bread and wine. On the other hand, we can describe what happens at Mass during the consecration using the ideas we just learned: substantial forms and accidents.

At Mass, the change of bread and wine into the Real Presence of Jesus is called "Transubstantiation." If you look closely at the word Transubstantiation, it is made of two parts: the prefix *trans*, which means change, and the root word *substance*. In other words, Transubstantiation is a "change of substance."

In the Eucharist, the substantial forms of the bread and wine are transformed into the substantial form of Christ's Body and Blood, Soul and Divinity. That means, the essential characteristics of bread and wine are changed into the essential characteristics of the Body and Blood of Jesus. The now consecrated hosts, however, keep the accidents of bread and wine. In other words, the look, smell, taste, size, shape, and so forth of bread and wine remain. This is why at Mass the bread still looks and tastes like bread. But, hidden beneath those non-essential characteristics of bread and wine is Jesus' Body and Blood, Soul and Divinity.

The Eucharist is 100% Jesus Christ, in substance. It is not just a symbol or an idea. We truly receive Jesus when we receive the Eucharist, just as He told us that He would give us His Flesh to eat and His Blood to drink as true food for the nourishment of our souls.

1. What are the words the priest says at Mass at the Eucharist called?

    The Conceneration

2. What happens to the bread and wine when the priest speaks these words?

    The bread and wine become body and blood

3. What is a substantial form? Describe the substantial form of a chair.

    what makes a chair a chair   the seat, legs, back.

4. What happens if you change the substantial form of something?

    It would be something else

5. What is an accidental form? Give an example.

it is a feature in something that does not change what it is
the color

6. What happens if you change an accidental form of something?

its accidential form changes but its substanctal form stays because
it is still a chair

7. What are the two root words of the word "Transubstantiation"?

Substance and trans

8. What does the word "Transubstantiation" mean?

Change of substance

9. How does the word "Transubstantiation" help explain what happens in the Eucharist?

it tells us how the wine and bread turn into the body and blood of
christ

Reflection Question

Why is the Eucharist not just a symbol or an idea?

_____

_____

_____

_____

_____

a frisbee - its plastic, purple, round, flat, throwable, light,
fun, has writting on it

United with God in the Eucharist

Directions: Read the essay and then answer the questions.

When we receive this Sacrament, we are taking into ourselves the Body and Blood of Jesus Christ. He is united with us, and we are united with Him. Because of this unity with Christ, all Christians are united with each other: we eat the Body of Christ, and become the Body of Christ, united with Him and with each other. Remember, too, that the Church includes the souls in Purgatory as well as the saints in Heaven. The Church offers the Eucharist as a sacrifice for the reparation of sins committed by the living and the dead.

Holy Communion strengthens and solidifies our union with Christ. Jesus said: "Whoever eats my flesh and drinks my blood remains in me and I in him. Just as the living Father sent me and I have life because of the Father, so also the one who feeds on me will have life because of me" (John 6:56-57). In other words, the main effect of receiving the Eucharist is that it unites us to Christ. Our whole Christian life is rooted in this unity with Jesus.

Jesus is all good, and so to be united with Him, we must also be pure. Therefore, it makes sense that another primary effect of receiving the Eucharist is that it separates us from sin and purifies us. The Eucharist forgives our past venial sins and helps to preserve us from future sin. Jesus tells us that His Blood "will be shed on behalf of many for the forgiveness of sins" (Matthew 26:28). We should not, however, receive the Eucharist in a state of mortal sin. We should prepare our hearts and souls to receive the Eucharist worthily, and that means being free from any serious sin. In Confession, Jesus forgives our mortal sins and points our souls once again toward Heaven.

1. Explain the two principle effects of the Eucharist.
   it unites us with Christ and washes away sin for purification

2. Jesus said, "I am the vine, you are the branches. Whoever remains in me and I in him will bear much fruit, because without me you can do nothing" (John 15:5). Does this Scripture verse remind you of the Eucharist in any way? Explain.
   It reminds me because it says with god we are given good things and empowered by them which is what the eucarist does

3. Now that you have learned more about this Sacrament, how does it help you to become more like your Heavenly Father?
   It pureifys me and roots me in unity with Christ

Eucharist Graphic Organizer

Directions: Use information from this guide, your class notes, and the *Catechism of the Catholic Church* nos. 1322-1419 to complete 1-5 on this chart. Share your personal reflections for 6-7.

1	Scriptural basis of this Sacrament.	The last Supper
2	Words spoken with this Sacrament (form). *The words of consencration*	This is my body which will be given up for you and this and this is the cup of blood
3	Things used or done when this Sacrament is received (matter).	wheat bread and grape wine
4	Effects of this Sacrament.	it unifys us closer with christ, and forgives our venial sins, and protects us from future sin
5	Ordinary minister of this Sacrament.	The priest
6	How does this Sacrament reveal God's life-giving love?	The best way to be with god is to consume him for God is all good
7	How does this Sacrament help you to become more like your Heavenly Father?	It unifys us with him

Sophia SketchPad Reflection Questions

Directions: Answer the questions below after watching and discussing the video.

1. How does God's mercy enter into our salvation? _God became man and took our_ _punishment for turning on him by dying on the cross._ _____
_____
_____

2. Why don't Christians sacrifice animals anymore? _because animals were sacrificed_ _in the place of men. When Jesus was killed he sacrifced himself for us_ _So the animals no longer need to be sacrificed_ _____

3. Why did Jesus command the Apostles to celebrate Mass for all Christians?
    So we can all participate in the sacriment of the eucharist _____
_____
_____

4. List some of the effects of receiving the Eucharist? What are some ways that we can live out those effects in our daily lives? → of grace

We recevie a sheld that helps block sin and live more united with christ.

5. What would you say to someone who said the Eucharist is just a symbol for Jesus' Body and Blood?

Actully it is not a symbol because the wine and bread we receve do transform into the body and blood of christ

6. Did you gain any new insights about the Sacrament of the Eucharist after watching this video? If so, what were they? If not, which part of the video did you think provided the clearest or most interesting information? Explain.

I think we humans are the bad guys

Penance and Reconciliation Pre-Assessment

Directions: In the left-hand column mark each statement true or false. Mark them again in the right column at the end of our study of Penance and Reconciliation to see if you were right.

Before beginning your study		*At the end of your study*
True or False?	**Statement**	**True or False?**
False	1. The Old Testament shows us a vengeful God; only in the New Testament is God's mercy revealed.	
True	2. Catholics do not believe you can confess your sins to God directly.	
True	3. The Sacrament of Penance and Reconciliation forgives sin and reconciles us to God and the Church.	
True	4. Jesus gave the Apostles the sacred power to forgive sins.	
True	5. In Confession you should confess venial and mortal sins.	
True	6. Penance allows us to participate in Christ's suffering in a small way.	
False	7. If you commit a mortal sin but you feel guilty about it for a long time, you do not need to go to Confession since your guilt was penance enough.	
True	8. The Church offers Penance and Reconciliation to those who would like to receive it, but it is not truly necessary to the Christian life.	

The Return of the Prodigal Son
BY REMBRANDT VAN RIJN (C. 1661-1669)

Hermitage Museum, St. Petersburg, Russia.

The Return of the Prodigal Son

 **The Return of the Prodigal Son**, *by Rembrandt van Rijn (C. 1661-1669)*

Directions: Reflect on the painting and read the parable in Luke 15:11-32, then answer the questions that follow.

Conversation Questions

1. The Rembrandt painting illustrates the parable of the Lost Son. What is your response to the painting? What is your favorite part?

2. How does it make you feel? What qualities of the painting do you think cause those feelings?

3. Do you think Rembrandt captured the essence of the parable? Why or why not?

4. At what point in the story do you think the younger son experienced conversion?

5. What does the father's response in the story tell us about how our Father in Heaven responds when we experience conversion and return to Him?

The Story of Penance and Reconciliation

Directions: Read the essay and answer the focus and reflection questions.

God deeply desires a relationship with each one of us. From Abraham to Moses to David to the prophets and finally to the sending of His Son to die for us, Salvation History clearly shows that God loves us and wants us to be with Him. Jesus' entire mission is based on reconciling us with the Father.

The institution of the Sacrament of Penance and Reconciliation

To help us be reconciled to the Father, Christ instituted ways to access His mercy whenever we are in need of it. In the Gospel of John, we learn that He entrusted this ministry to the Apostles. Jesus gave St. Peter, the first pope, the authority to make decisions that would be binding on earth as well as in Heaven. The *Catechism* teaches us that "the words *bind and loose* mean: whomever you exclude from your communion, will be excluded from communion with God; whomever you receive anew into your communion, God will welcome back into his. *Reconciliation with the Church is inseparable from reconciliation with God*" (CCC 1445).

When the resurrected Christ first appeared to the disciples, he said to them: "'Peace be with you. As the Father has sent me, so I send you.' And when he had said this, he breathed on them and said to them, 'Receive the holy Spirit. Whose sins you forgive are forgiven them, and whose sins you retain are retained'" (John 20:21-23). But the Apostles wouldn't

be on earth forever either, so they gave this same power to their successors and to priests so that all people from that day to ours can experience God's forgiveness. More than two thousand years have gone by, and the Apostles' successors and priests continue to exercise the ministry of Reconciliation. Every week in your own parish, Christ continues His work through your priest as he hears confessions and forgives sins in the person of Christ.

Why do we need Confession?

Confession is necessary because we need to be brought back to God when we sin. Despite our baptisms, and despite our best intentions, we have an inclination to sin. Throughout our lives, we will have to resist this tendency. Turning away from sin and toward God and the holiness He calls us to is a lifelong struggle of conversion. Confession first involves feeling contrition – sorrow for sins and the resolve not to sin again. Although it may sound contrary to common sense, "bad" feelings such as sorrow and shame about bad things we have done are signs of God's grace. Those feelings of contrition, or even attrition (fear of punishment), inspire us to seek out God's mercy in the Sacrament of Confession. When we confess our sins to a priest, we are making a choice to turn back to God and ask for His forgiveness. In the person of the priest, Christ forgives our sins.

The priest then assigns us a penance – usually to say a prayer or to do something kind for another person. Jesus already took away our sins when He suffered and died on the Cross for us. When we do penance, His sacrifice gets worked into our soul. We are joining in Christ's suffering in a small way to make amends for our sins and become His disciples once more.

Going frequently to Confession helps form a stronger conscience. When we have experienced forgiveness, it also becomes easier to forgive others. Experiencing mercy helps us show mercy. This truth helps us live up to the ideals of Christian life in the Beatitudes. Jesus calls us to be forgiving, as He is: "Blessed are the merciful, for they will be shown mercy" (Matthew 5:7).

Love and forgiveness

You may have experienced the difficulty of forgiving someone who has betrayed you. This sense that forgiveness is difficult might lead us to think that God finds it equally challenging to forgive us. But it is not. Jesus is the Word of God, and God is love (1 John 4:8). When He says, "I love you," we are healed, transformed, and enriched, and we can say, with Mary: "The Mighty One has done great things for me" (Luke 1:49).

Indeed, we must remember that God already knows what our sins are. He loves us anyway. Jesus told us that He came not for the righteous, but for sinners (Luke 5:32). He also said, "[T]here will be more joy in heaven over one sinner who repents than over ninety-nine righteous people who have no need of repentance" (Luke 15:7).

With your consent and cooperation, Jesus gives you the great gift of His love and mercy. All He requires is that you desire this as well! Through His bishops and priests, Jesus waits for you in the confessional.

1. Our sins are washed away in Baptism. Why do we need Confession?

   because we are still enclind to sin and ____ ____ be

2. Jesus told St. Peter: "I will give you the keys to the kingdom of heaven. Whatever you bind on earth shall be bound in heaven; and whatever you loose on earth shall be loosed in heaven" (Matthew 16:19). Can you make any connection between this verse and the Sacrament of Penance and Reconciliation?

   the words bind and loose means when you sin on earth you carry that sin with you until it is washes away

3. What is the purpose of penance?

4. In addition to the principle effects of forgiveness of sins and reconciliation with God and the Church, what are other benefits of Confession?

Santifying grace, unifyes us with christ, forgiveness, forms ar consiousness

Reflection Question

Why do you think the Sacrament of Penance and Reconciliation is sometimes called the Sacrament of Conversion?

Why Confess to a Priest?

Directions: Read the information, and then sketch a scene that shows the way Jesus forgives us and reconciles us to the Him and the Church in the Sacrament of Penance and Reconciliation.

Many ask why we must confess our sins to a priest instead of going to God directly. When you go to Confession, you are going to God directly. Jesus gave priests many spiritual powers – the power to baptize, to turn bread and wine into His Body and Blood, and to forgive sins.

We call these the Sacraments. They are not only spiritual encounters with God – they are physical encounters with Him. Just as you can taste the Eucharist or feel water in Baptism, you can hear the priest tell you that you are forgiven. God isn't just in Heaven; He is here with us acting in the world. Confession is one way we foster a true and human friendship with Jesus Christ.

Penance and Reconciliation, one of the two Sacraments of Healing, helps restore our souls to a state of grace. Penance and Reconciliation is also called the Sacrament of Confession, the Sacrament of Penance and Reconciliation, and the Sacrament of Conversion (CCC 1423-1424). This Sacrament is for anyone who has ever freely chosen to sin and therefore feely chosen to separate themselves from God and the Church. Through Penance and Reconciliation, Jesus joyfully welcomes us back if we only ask for His mercy.

because when you confess your sins to the priest your are confessing to God too. Because God gave priests the ability to forgive sins, God also wants this to be a physical encounter for us. The priest connects us with the comunity. The priest resembles God.

mortal sin = Dystroys our connection with God
venial sin = wounds our connection with God

when we sin we know what we are doing its wrong and we do it any way.

no one is beyond God's grace

God's Mercy Revealed in the Old Testament

Directions: Look up and read the given Scripture passages, then complete the chart.

	How would you put this verse in your own words?	How does this verse reveal God's mercy?	How does this verse connect to the Sacrament of Penance and Reconciliation?
1	Isaiah 43:25:		
2	Isaiah 1:18:		
3	Psalm 51:19:		
4	Proverbs 28:13:		

Why We Need Confession

Directions: Read the essay, then answer the focus and reflection questions.

You know this story: God made the world. God made man. God placed man in the Garden of Eden and gave him rules for his benefit. Then the Serpent – Satan – played to man's pride, twisting and distorting God's plan in man's mind. Adam and Eve listened to the Serpent and chose to disobey God. God banished man from the garden and His presence.

This would be a very sad story if it ended there. Thankfully there is more to the story! God deeply desires a relationship with each one of us. The problem is that we often still listen to Satan rather than to God. When we freely choose to reject God, we must be reconciled to Him, that is, brought back into friendship with Him.

To help us be reconciled to the Father, Jesus gave us a way to access His mercy whenever we need it: Confession. We need Confession anytime that we need to be brought back into God's grace. All sins are a failure to love, and they all hurt our relationship with God. But the most serious sins, called mortal sins, result in separation from God, because we have freely chosen to separate ourselves.

Remember that God created you in His image with intellect, free will, and the capacity to love. Sin and evil exist because of free will. If we were not free to choose between good and evil, we would not be responsible for our actions. Because we are free to choose, we are responsible for them. You don't live in the Garden of Eden, but you have the same choice to make as Adam and Eve. You can use your free will to disobey God, as Adam and Eve did, or you can choose to return His love by believing in Him and keeping His commandments.

God rejoices when sinners repent, and He will never give up on you. Think about biblical sinners who experienced conversion and went on to become holy, such as King David, who abandoned his men in battle, was unfaithful to his wife, tried to cover it up, and then had his mistress's husband killed. St. Peter denied Jesus three times. St. Matthew was a greedy tax collector turned Apostle. St. Paul viciously persecuted the Church before becoming the greatest missionary of all time. God's grace has no limit.

The story of Adam and Eve was not the end of the story of our salvation. With our consent and cooperation, Jesus gives us the great gift. He not only writes a happy ending to the story of our lives, but He rewrites our past, making our entire life into a "story of salvation." The stories in which the characters live happily ever after are the best stories! Confession is the key to make sure our relationships with both God and one another end in reconciliation, or "happily ever after."

1. What choice did Adam and Eve have? _to listen to God or Satan_

2. What is the result of mortal sin? _It separates you from God_

3. How do you face the same choice as Adam and Eve? _I can be with or without God_

Reflection Questions

4. "Don't be afraid of confession," Pope Francis said. "When someone is in line for confession he feels all these things – even shame – but then, when he finishes confessing, he leaves free, great, beautiful, forgiven, clean, happy." Why would someone feel happy after Confession? Have you ever felt this way? Explain.

   Because he has been forgiven by God. Of course he's gonna be happy! yes I have felt this way before.

5. One may still feel guilty after confessing a sin and receiving absolution. Why might this be?

   Maybe because he feels like he should not have been forgiven for his sins

6. Now that you have learned more about this Sacrament, how does it help you to become more like your Heavenly Father?

   When you confess your sins to God you are unifyed with him

Mortal Sin
1 Grave matter
2 Full Knowledge
3 Full consent

venial Sin
small matter
no knowledge
or consent

Symbols of the Sacrament of Penance and Reconciliation

Directions: Priests who have received the faculty of absolving from the authority of the Church can forgive sins in the name of Christ. Read the information, then complete the chart with your own original drawings.

Symbol	Background	Your drawing
Keys – a single key or a pair of crossed keys	Jesus told St. Peter: "I will give you the keys to the kingdom of heaven. Whatever you bind on earth shall be bound in heaven; and whatever you loose on earth shall be loosed in heaven" (Matthew 16:19).	
Purple stole – a long, thin strip of cloth that a priest wears over his shoulders	Purple is the liturgical color of sorrow and repentance.	
A raised hand	The priest holds his right hand over your head as he absolves you of your sins in the person of Christ.	
The Cross	The priest makes the Sign of the Cross over you as he closes the Prayer of Absolution, "And I absolve you from your sins in the name of the Father, and of the Son, and of the Holy Spirit."	

Penance and Reconciliation Graphic Organizer

Directions: Use information from this guide, your class notes, and the *Catechism of the Catholic Church* nos. 1422-1498 to complete 1-5 on this chart. Share your personal reflections for 6-7.

1	Scriptural basis of this Sacrament.	John 223 Risen Jesus breathed on the apostles, allowing them to forgive Sins
2	Words spoken with this Sacrament (form).	Through the ministry of the church may God pardon and Peace and insolve you of all your Sins in the father the Son & the holy Spirit
3	Things used or done when this Sacrament is received (matter).	The Penance
4	Effects of this Sacrament.	
5	Ordinary minister of this Sacrament.	a priest
6	How does this Sacrament reveal God's life-giving love?	
7	How does this Sacrament help you to become more like your Heavenly Father?	

Sophia SketchPad Reflection Question

Directions: Answer the question below after watching and discussing the video.

Did you gain any new insights about the Sacrament of Penance and Reconciliation after watching this video? If so, what were they? If not, which part of the video did you think provided the clearest or most interesting information? Explain.

_____

_____

_____

_____

_____

_____

Anointing of the Sick Pre-Assessment

Directions: In the left-hand column mark each statement true or false. Mark them again in the right-hand column at the end of our study of Penance and Reconciliation to see if you were right.

Before beginning your study		*At the end of your study*
True or False?	**Statement**	**True or False?**
True	1. Sickness and suffering entered the world because of Original Sin.	
True	2. Suffering can be, but is not always, the result of personal sin.	
False	3. The Sacrament of Anointing of the Sick forgives sin.	
True	4. Anointing of the Sick can be received for any illness.	
True	5. The ordinary minister of Anointing of the Sick is a priest.	
False	6. Because He was fully divine, Jesus did not really suffer during His life.	
True	7. The Church offers Anointing of the Sick to those who would like to receive it, but it is not truly necessary to the Christian life.	

On the Christian Meaning of Human Suffering

Directions: Read the selections from Pope St. John Paul II's *Salvifici Doloris* (On the Christian Meaning of Human Suffering) and the information that follows, then answer the questions.

Part I

Jesus' suffering has human dimensions; it also is unique in the history of humanity – a depth and intensity that, while being human, can also be an incomparable depth and intensity of suffering, insofar as the man who suffers is in person the only begotten Son himself: "God from God." Therefore, only he – the only begotten Son – is capable of embracing the measure of evil contained in the sin of man: In every sin and in "total" sin, according to the dimensions of the historical existence of humanity on earth.

–SALVIFICI DOLORIS 17

1. Make a list of all the ways Jesus suffered in the following ways:

   Physically _they put a cross on him, thorns, and beat him with sticks_

   Mentally _No one really cared nor followed him anymore_

   Spiritually _He has to carry all our sins_

2. Why does Pope St. John Paul II say that only Jesus is "capable of embracing the measure of evil contained in the sin of man"?

   Because we are all enclind to sin and Jesus is the only one who can help us not to.

Part II

Christ has accomplished the world's redemption through his own suffering. For, at the same time, this redemption, even though it was completely achieved by Christ's suffering, lives on and in its own special way develops in the history of man. It lives and develops as the body of Christ, the Church, and in this dimension every human suffering, by reason of the loving union with Christ, completes the suffering of Christ. It completes that suffering just as the Church completes the redemptive work of Christ....

Christ's revelation of the salvific meaning of suffering is in no way identified with an attitude of passivity. Completely the reverse is true. The gospel is the negation of passivity in the face of suffering. Christ himself is especially active in this field.

–SALVIFICI DOLORIS 30

3. Through what has Christ accomplished the world's redemption?

   He suffered on the the cross

4. If human suffering is united by love to Christ, what does that suffering accomplish?

   unity with Christ.

5. To negate something means to cancel it out, and being passive means allowing things to happen without taking any action. From what you know of Jesus' life, how would you assess the statement "The gospel is the negation of passivity in the face of suffering"?

   Their saying the gosple stop suffering from happing without someone doing something about it.

Part III

Jesus came to free us from suffering, sickness, and separation from God in death through His own suffering, Death, and Resurrection. He took on the eternal consequence of sin and opened Heaven to us. Jesus continues to be active in the world. In the Sacrament of Anointing of the Sick, we receive an outpouring of God's grace to strengthen us to face suffering and sickness and even death that results from the Original Sin.

6. What is the purpose of the Sacrament of Anointing of the Sick?

   to Strenghten us to battle against death, Sickness, and Suffering

7. From just the reading and information we have discussed today, how would you begin to answer the questions:

   › How does this Sacrament reveal God's life-giving love?

   He helps us when we are Suffeing or sick.

   › How does this Sacrament help me to become more like my Heavenly Father?

   It gives us strength like him.

The Story of Anointing of the Sick

Directions: Read the essay, then answer the questions that follow.

The Sacrament of Anointing of the Sick is a frequently misunderstood Sacrament of the Church. This Sacrament is appropriate not only for those at the point of death; it can be received any time a person is in danger of death because of very serious illness or old age. The graces from the Sacrament are given to help us overcome and endure the suffering that is a part of the human condition, while uniting our misery to Christ's redemptive actions.

Original Sin

God created our original parents without sin, and they enjoyed an intimate relationship with Him in paradise, free from suffering, illness, and death. This idyllic situation changed, however, when Adam and Eve gave in to the temptation of the serpent and ate of the fruit from the Tree of Knowledge of Good and Evil. This singular action, the Original Sin, broke the unity between Heaven and earth and ushered in sickness, suffering, sin, and death. This fallen state was now the human condition: the natural consequences of our own actions, passed on to all humans for every generation.

God's love for us

God loved the world so much that He gave His only beloved Son into the world to become human, like us in all things but sin, to willingly suffer and die for all mankind on the Cross. In this redemptive act, Christ transformed human suffering into something new. No longer are suffering, illness, and death just a byproduct of sin, the work of the devil. Now, united to Christ's own suffering, the suffering inherent in the human condition can make us more Christlike and be offered for others and the Church as a redemptive sacrifice.

Anointing of the Sick

We will all encounter the consequences of sin: the suffering and sickness that are a part of the human condition. And we will all face death. This Jesus knew, and experienced Himself. In fact, Jesus closely identified with the sick and suffering, not only during His own Passion, but during His public ministry when He healed so many who were sick and infirm. Jesus sent His Apostles out two by two to heal the sick and forgive sins as a sign of the arrival of the Kingdom of God, prophesied from the Old Testament. And He commanded His Church to heal the sick. And so, working through human signs and actions as He always does, Jesus gave us the Sacrament of Anointing of the Sick as a means of communicating God's grace and an outpouring of the Holy Spirit to strengthen the sick and suffering person in the face of adversity and to prepare the person for the final struggles before beholding the Beatific Vision of God.

In this Sacrament, the priest, who is the proper minister, anoints with holy oil and lays his hands upon the sick person as a sign of the outpouring of the Holy Spirit and an affirming of the indelible seal placed upon the person's soul at Baptism and Confirmation that mark him or her as God's possession. This anointing strengthens the person to endure, gives peace and courage to overcome, and if it is God's will, be healed. It also unites the suffering of the person to Christ's own suffering, making it redemptive in nature and a participation in Christ's saving work.

The Sacrament also brings with it the presence of the Church in the person of the priest, thereby helping to break down feelings of isolation and loneliness. The gesture of anointing and the soothing aspect of the oil communicate the touch, intimacy, and closeness of Christ and His Church.

God loves us so much that He became one of us. Because Jesus was fully human, He experienced all that we experience (except sin). So if Jesus did something, it must be good. Because He suffered so terribly, we can connect our suffering to His Passion on the Cross. In this way, we can participate in the redemptive quality of suffering for ourselves and for others.

St. Gregory of Nazianzus wrote, "What has not been assumed has not been healed." Christ healed humanity because He assumed humanity. Christ redeemed suffering because He suffered. Christ won victory over death because He died. And Christ will glorify man's body because He rose in glory.

1. Who should receive the Sacrament of Anointing of the Sick?

   People who are faced with death because of old age or illness.

2. How did suffering enter the world?

   Through the actions of Adam and Eve.

3. How did Christ transform the meaning of suffering?

   Suffering meant sickness and death until Jesus transformed it into a way to unify us with him.

4. How is this Sacrament administered?

   Through the priest.

5. How does this Sacrament communicate the closeness of Jesus and the Church?

   When someone is anointed the smoothness of the oil and the anointing show touch. Closeness between Jesus & the church, and intimacy

Reflection Question

Have you ever been very ill? While you were feeling sick, was there anything that made you feel better? If you haven't been very ill, what do you imagine would make you feel better?

I have and one thing that made me feel better was the kindness of others.

Sin and Suffering in the Old Testament

Directions: Read the information, and then look up the Bible verses. After reading each one, answer the focus questions and explain how Jesus Christ helps us understand this aspect of sin and suffering more fully. Finally, answer the reflection question.

In the Old Testament and up through the time of Jesus, the people believed that sickness and suffering were the direct result of sin. Therefore, they looked to God for healing of their sickness and suffering by the forgiveness of their sins. Some even believed that God would save them from death, which was also the direct result of the sin of Adam and Eve. In the end, through the prophecy of Isaiah, the people believed that when the Messiah came to usher in God's kingdom, He would be announced by miraculous healings and the forgiveness of all sin.

While sin can certainly be the direct cause of our sickness and suffering (both personal sin, and structures of sin), often sickness and suffering serve another purpose: so that the works of God might be made visible through our suffering. In Jesus, our suffering and sickness can be redemptive. In other words, we can come to know God and experience conversion because of our suffering and sickness. This is a change from the Old Testament understanding of suffering and sickness. In Christ, suffering takes on new meaning. In fact, it is a requirement of being a disciple.

1. Genesis 3:16-19

What are the consequences for the Original Sin of Adam and Eve?

_____

How does Jesus help us understand this aspect of sin and suffering more fully?

_____

2. Psalm 38:2-5

What is the cause of the psalmist's suffering and sickness?

_____

How does Jesus help us understand this aspect of sin and suffering more fully?

_____

3. Psalm 107:17-22

Why did some fall sick? What did the LORD send to heal them?

_____

How does Jesus help us understand this aspect of sin and suffering more fully?

_____

4. Isaiah 33:24

What does the sacred author prophesy will happen to those who dwell in God's Kingdom?

_____

How does Jesus help us understand this aspect of sin and suffering more fully?

_____

5. Isaiah 53:10-11

What can happen because of suffering?

_____

How does Jesus help us understand this aspect of sin and suffering more fully?

_____

Reflection Question

Look up John 9:1–7 and explain what this passage reveals about sin and suffering.

_____

_____

_____

_____

_____

The Miraculous Healings of Jesus

Directions: Read the information followed by the Gospel accounts, and then answer the questions.

For those facing death, Anointing of the Sick completes life's sacramental journey. We begin our spiritual lives in Baptism, strengthen the Gifts of the Holy Spirit at Confirmation, and are fully initiated through the Eucharist. We are forgiven of sin in Reconciliation and accept our vocation in Holy Matrimony or Holy Orders. Anointing of the Sick strengthens us at the end of our earthly life. The dying person is prepared to meet God face to face.

The principal symbols of the Sacrament of Anointing of the Sick are the anointing with oil and the laying on of hands. The anointing of oil in Anointing of the Sick confirms the indelible seal placed on the soul in Baptism and in Confirmation. The person is affirmed as belonging to God. An outpouring of the Holy Spirit is sent upon the person to fortify him or her for the journey ahead. The anointed is tasked with the mission of Christ, to proclaim in his suffering and even death the salvation won for us by Christ's own suffering and Death on the Cross. The celebrant prays for God's grace to come upon the soul of the suffering person.

As you read the following Gospel stories to follow, look for ways the rite of this Sacrament is drawn from Christ's miraculous healings.

Read Luke 7:11-17.

1. Briefly summarize the story.

_____

_____

2. What did Jesus say to the sick person or to the crowd?

_____

3. What command or action did Jesus do to heal the person?

_____

4. How did the newly healed person or the crowd respond to the healing?

_____

5. What do you think this miraculous healing communicates about the Kingdom of God?

_____

Read Mark 8:22-26.

6. Briefly summarize the story.

    _____

    _____

7. What did Jesus say to the sick person or to the crowd?

    _____

8. What command or action did Jesus do to heal the person?

    _____

9. How did the newly healed person or the crowd respond to the healing?

    _____

10. What do you think this miraculous healing communicates about the Kingdom of God?

    _____

Read Mark 2:1-12.

11. Briefly summarize the story.

    _____

    _____

12. What did Jesus say to the sick person or to the crowd?

    _____

13. What command or action did Jesus do to heal the person?

    _____

14. How did the newly healed person or the crowd respond to the healing?

    _____

15. What do you think this miraculous healing communicates about the Kingdom of God?

    _____

Read Mark 7:31-37.

16. Briefly summarize the story.

_____

_____

17. What did Jesus say to the sick person or to the crowd?

_____

18. What command or action did Jesus do to heal the person?

_____

19. How did the newly healed person or the crowd respond to the healing?

_____

20. What do you think this miraculous healing communicates about the Kingdom of God?

_____

Read Luke 13:10-17.

21. Briefly summarize the story.

_____

_____

22. What did Jesus say to the sick person or to the crowd?

_____

23. What command or action did Jesus do to heal the person?

_____

24. How did the newly healed person or the crowd respond to the healing?

_____

25. What do you think this miraculous healing communicates about the Kingdom of God?

_____

Read Luke 17:11-19.

26. Briefly summarize the story.

10 lepers come and ask for Jesus's mercy and then he cleanses them and they are grateful.

27. What did Jesus say to the sick person or to the crowd?

go and show yourselves to the priests

28. What command or action did Jesus do to heal the person?

He sent them to be cleansed by the priest

29. How did the newly healed person or the crowd respond to the healing?

He fell to his knees gratful for what had happened to him

30. What do you think this miraculous healing communicates about the Kingdom of God?

Everyone deserves to be in the kingdom of God.

The Redemption of Suffering

Directions: Read the essay, then answer the questions that follow.

Sickness and suffering is a part of human nature. The *Catechism of the Catholic Church* explains in paragraphs 1500 and 1501 that, "Every illness can make us glimpse death. Illness can lead to anguish, self-absorption, sometimes even despair and revolt against God. It can also make a person more mature, helping him discern ... what is not essential so that he can turn toward that which is. Very often illness provokes a search for God and a return to him."

Pope St. John Paul II wrote in *Salvifici Doloris* (On the Christian Meaning of Human Suffering) that God can even help us find joy in suffering:

"A source of joy is found in the overcoming of the sense of the uselessness of suffering. ...This feeling not only consumes the person interiorly but seems to make him a burden to others. The person feels condemned to receive help and assistance from others and at the same time seems useless to himself. The discovery of the salvific meaning of suffering in union with Christ transforms this depressing feeling. ... [The suffering person] is serving, like Christ, the salvation of his brothers and sisters. Therefore he is carrying out an irreplaceable service" (27).

1. What does the *Catechism* say illness can sometimes lead to? Have you ever experienced these effects?

   It can lead to anguish, self absorption, despair, revolt against God, Maturity, and search for god. yes I have

2. What can be some good outcomes of illness?

   It brings you closer to God and help you mature

3. Our society can often act as though suffering is meaningless, and that people with serious illnesses are a burden. Have you ever observed signs of this false notion? Explain.

Yes. I have seen this before and I wish it would go away.

4. Pope St. John Paul II explained that suffering not only has meaning but is also an "irreplaceable service." What did he mean?

Suffering can not be replaced for it has been given a purpose by God.

Anointing of the Sick Graphic Organizer

Directions: Use information from this guide, your class notes, and the *Catechism of the Catholic Church* nos. 1499-1532 to complete 1-5 on this chart. Share your personal reflections for 6-7.

1 Scriptural basis of this Sacrament.	
2 Words spoken with this Sacrament (form).	
3 Things used or done when this Sacrament is received (matter).	
4 Effects of this Sacrament.	
5 Ordinary minister of this Sacrament.	
6 How does this Sacrament reveal God's life-giving love?	
7 How does this Sacrament help you to become more like your Heavenly Father?	

Holy Matrimony Pre-Assessment

Directions: In the left-hand column mark each statement true or false. Mark them again in the right-hand column at the end of our study of Holy Matrimony to see if you were right.

Before beginning your study

True or False?

At the end of your study

True or False?

Statement

_____   1.   Marriage is part of human nature.   _____

_____   2.   Salvation History begins and ends with a wedding.   _____

_____   3.   Jesus began His public ministry at a wedding.   _____

_____   4.   The Sacrament of Holy Matrimony forgives sin.   _____

_____   5.   The spouses themselves are the ministers of this Sacrament.   _____

_____   6.   The way God loves shows us how spouses should love.   _____

_____   7.   Left on their own, spouses cannot love as God wants them to love. They need His help.   _____

_____   8.   The Church offers to marry couples who wish to live together, but marriage is not truly necessary for those couples to live a Christian life.   _____

Salvation History Begins and Ends with a Wedding Image Collage

The Creation of Eve, Orthodox icon.

The Wedding Feast at Cana, by Julius Schnorr von Carolsfeld (c. 1819). Kunsthalle Hamburg Museum, Germany.

Detail from The Ghent Altarpiece, by Jan van Eyck (c. 1430–1432). Saint Bavo Cathedral, Belgium.

Salvation History Begins and Ends with a Wedding

Directions: Reflect on the images, then respond to the questions.

1. Read Genesis 2:22-24 below. How does the icon *Creation of Adam and Eve* help you understand these verses?

    The LORD God then built the rib that he had taken from the man into a woman. When he brought her to the man, the man said: "This one, at last, is bone of my bones and flesh of my flesh; This one shall be called 'woman,' for out of man this one has been taken." That is why a man leaves his father and mother and clings to his wife, and the two of them become one body.

    _____

    _____

    _____

2. Read the Gospel story of the Wedding at Cana in John 2:1-12. What moment in the Gospel story has the artist captured? How does the painting help you better understand the story of the Wedding at Cana?

    _____

    _____

    _____

3. Read Revelation 19:7-9 below.

    "Let us rejoice and be glad and give him glory. For the wedding day of the Lamb has come, his bride has made herself ready. She was allowed to wear a bright, clean linen garment." [The linen represents the righteous deeds of the holy ones.] Then the angel said to me, "Write this: Blessed are those who have been called to the wedding feast of the Lamb." And he said to me, "These words are true; they come from God."

    Who is the bride of the Lamb? _____

4. Do these words sound familiar? "Blessed are those who have been called to the wedding feast of the Lamb." Where have you heard them before?

_____

_____

5. From what part of Adam was Eve formed? Read John 19:34: "[B]ut one soldier thrust his lance into his side, and immediately blood and water flowed out." Can you make any connection between this verse, the creation of Eve, and the Sacrament of Holy Matrimony?

_____

_____

_____

The Story of Holy Matrimony

Directions: Read the essay, then answer the focus and reflection questions.

It is not just a coincidence that the written record of salvation, the Bible, begins with the first marriage and ends with the wedding feast of the lamb in the book of Revelation. The story of salvation communicates the greater relationship that God desires to have with us. Jesus begins His public ministry with a miracle at the Wedding at Cana, lifting the primordial sacrament (primordial means it has existed since the beginning of time) to a Sacrament of the Church.

Marriage and human nature

Marriage is an integral part of what it means to be human. To be made in God's image and likeness is, in part, to be male and female, in order to carry out God's one command in the beginning: to be fertile and multiply and fill the earth. Genesis 2 more fully describes the creation of woman and the unity shared between the sexes. God tells Adam that it is not good that he is alone, so He will create a helper for him. God brings all of the animals to Adam in search of a companion, not because God thought any of the animals was a suitable mate for Adam, but rather so that Adam would recognize the he is unique out of all creation. While sharing certain characteristics with the animals, man is also undeniably and substantially different from all of them. Only then does God create woman from Adam's side. Rather than the popular notion that woman was made somehow less than man, man and woman are in fact equal in dignity and close to one another's hearts.

©Basilica of the National Shrine of the Immaculate Conception, Washington, D.C. Photograph courtesy of the National Shrine. Photographer: Geraldine M. Rohling.

When Adam meets his wife for the first time, she causes him to speak in verse, bringing forth the best of man in recognition of the beauty before him. Adam proclaims that at last there is one like him, a person who is unique out of all creation, but shared in the same dignity and vocation to love and holiness as he, "bone of my bones, flesh of my flesh." Man and woman become "one body," and cling to one another united in marriage to fulfill God's command to fruitfulness. The foundation of marriage, both as natural law and a sacramental covenant, is found in the very beginnings of the creation of man and woman and is an integral part of what it means to be human.

Jesus elevates marriage to a Sacrament

The story of salvation, having begun with the first marriage of the original man and woman, ends with a vision of Heaven in the book of Revelation. This vision shows us that Heaven is the wedding celebration of the Lamb, Jesus, who is united for all eternity with His Bride, us, His Church. We recognize in Holy Matrimony a sign of Jesus' union with His Church, which is consummated every time we receive Him in the Eucharist. We are truly blessed as Christians to be invited to partake of the wedding feast of the Lamb every time we receive the Eucharist, the Body and Blood of Jesus Christ.

Not only does the Bible begin with a wedding and end with a wedding feast, but Jesus began His public ministry with a miracle at a wedding. This is no coincidence! Jesus is first revealed to the public as the Messiah, the Son of God and Savior, in the midst of a wedding. By doing so, Jesus announced that the time had come for God's relationship with His people to be restored. The *Catechism of the Catholic Church* no. 1613 states: "The Church attaches great importance to Jesus' presence at the wedding at Cana. She sees in it the confirmation of the goodness of marriage and the proclamation that thenceforth marriage will be an efficacious [effective] sign of Christ's presence." It is for this reason that the Church places such a great importance on the Sacrament of Matrimony and defends the union of one man and one woman so vigorously.

1. Why is marriage called the primordial sacrament?

   because it has been around since the beginning of time.

2. How do we know men and women are equal in dignity?

   _____

   _____

3. What is the vision of Heaven in the book of Revelation, and how does it connect to marriage?

   The vision is the wedding celebration of the lamb, and it unitys us with God like in marriage

4. Where did Jesus perform His first public miracle, revealing Himself to be the Messiah?

at a wedding

Reflection Questions

5. Jesus is first revealed to the public as the Messiah, the Son of God and Savior, in the midst of a wedding. Why would a wedding be the perfect setting for this announcement?

Because a wedding is a great celebration and so is the miracle of the messiah.

6. Can you think of any ways that married love and divine love are similar?

God's Love and the Goods of Marriage

Marriage as an icon of the Trinity

God is love. At His heart, God is three Persons in one God who eternally share their love for each other. From all eternity the Father pours out all He is in generating the Son, who in turn pours out all He is in love toward the Father. The Holy Spirit is the third Divine Person. He eternally proceeds from the Father and the Son and is one and equal with them. This exchange of love between the Divine Persons is perfect and eternal, without beginning or end. Divine love shows us that love creates communion and always generates life.

Marriage and Divine Love

The Lord created man and woman in love. We are made in the divine image, so, in imitation of the Blessed Trinity, we too are called to love totally and completely, following the pattern of Trinitarian love.

In Holy Matrimony, Christ's sacrifice on the Cross is made visible in human love. Jesus, on the night before He died, freely gave His Body to His bride, the Church, in the Eucharist. The next day He sacrificed Himself for her by embracing His Cross. Original Sin damaged our understanding of what love is and our ability to love. We tend to mistakenly think love is just a "feeling" we can fall in and out of, rather than a free choice we make every day. We also tend to be selfish and sinful. The good news is that Jesus restored the true meaning of love to us by His Cross and Resurrection and revealed to us the Trinitarian life of love. On the Cross,

He showed us that love means doing what is good for the other. When Jesus' side was pierced on the Cross (John 19:34), blood and water flowed out. The Fathers of the Church teach that the blood and water signify the Sacraments of Eucharist and Baptism, the Sacraments that create the Church. In a way, we can say that out of Jesus' side is formed His Bride, the Church, just as Eve was formed out of the side of Adam. Jesus is married to the Church. Married love reflects and reveals divine love. God's love is freely given, faithful, total self-giving, and fruitful. The love shared between a man and a woman in marriage is a reflection of the love of God.

Marriage is a public state of life in the Church. That is why couples exchange their vows before a priest or deacon, within a liturgical celebration such as a Mass, and in front of family, friends, and the Catholic community who will support the married couple.

The goods of marriage
Love freely given

God's love is a free gift to us. We do nothing to earn His love, and there is nothing we can do to lose His love. These Scripture passages attest to God's free gift of love:

> Romans 6:23 – For the wages of sin is death, but the gift of God is eternal life in Christ Jesus our Lord.

> 1 John 4:19 – We love because he first loved us.

Marital love must be freely given. The consent of the spouses is the fundamental requirement for marriage. In fact, in sacramental marriage, the ministers of the sacrament are the spouses who give their consent to one another and exchange vows of lifelong commitment before God and His Church. The priest or deacon serves as the official witness of this exchange and offers the blessing of the Church on the marital union.

Faithful love

God's love is faithful. God does not withdraw His love from us at any time for any reason. Even though we are less than faithful to Him when we sin, He remains near to us and showers us with His grace. These Scripture passages attest to God's faithful love:

> Romans 8:37-39 – No, in all these things we conquer overwhelmingly through him who loved us. For I am convinced that neither death, nor life, nor angels, nor principalities, nor present things, nor future things, nor powers, nor height, nor depth, nor any other creature will be able to separate us from the love of God in Christ Jesus our Lord.

> Deuteronomy 7:9 – Know, then, that the LORD, your God, is God: the faithful God who keeps covenant mercy to the thousandth generation toward those who love him and keep his commandments.

Married love is faithful, constant, dependable, and trustworthy. Marriage is a total gift of self, body and soul, to another of the opposite, complementary sex. It cannot be a total gift of self if something is held back or reserved for another. Love's fidelity or faithfulness is expressed in the fact that

marriage can be between only one man and one woman. Moreover, this relationship doesn't start and then stop. It is a relationship "until death do us part."

Total self-giving love

God's love is total and self-giving. God gives all of Himself to us. He holds nothing back. He loved us so much that He assumed a human nature and gave all that He had, His very life, for us on the Cross. These Scripture passages attest to God's total self-giving love:

> Philippians 2:7-8 – Rather, he emptied himself, taking the form of a slave, coming in human likeness; and found human in appearance, he humbled himself, becoming obedient to death, even death on a cross.

> John 3:16 – For God so loved the world that he gave his only Son, so that everyone who believes in him might not perish but might have eternal life.

Marital love is also total and self-giving. The bond of love given and received in marriage cannot be broken. The Blessed Trinity reveals that love means to give oneself to others. But we also know that sin has harmed our ability to love. So, to love truly in this fallen world will involve sacrifice. It will involve working against our tendency to be selfish and unfaithful. Because of our sinfulness, loving will also mean forgiving and asking for forgiveness when we do wrong. It involves both spouses sharing every aspect of their lives with each other. Because it is a total gift of self, the bond of marriage is therefore indissoluble and permanent. As Jesus explains, "what God has joined together, no human being must separate" (Matthew 19:6). Everything that God creates is good, including the union of man and woman in marriage.

Fruitful love

God's love is fruitful. God is the Creator of all things, and He holds all things in continued existence solely because He loves us. He is love itself, and the Holy Spirit eternally procceeds from the Father and the Son and is one and equal with them. These Scripture passages attest to God's fruitful love:

> John 1:3-5 – All things came to be through him, and without him nothing came to be. What came to be through him was life, and this life was the light of the human race; the light shines in the darkness, and the darkness has not overcome it.

> Genesis 1:31 – God looked at everything he had made, and found it very good. Evening came, and morning followed–the sixth day.

Marital love must also be fruitful. The sexual union of male and female, in cooperation with God's divine plan, results in the procreation of children. This is the natural result of the love shared between spouses. A husband and wife create a special world, in imitation of the Blessed Trinity. In the home, in their arms and under their loving, watchful eyes, husband and wife create the first world their children will ever know. The *Catechism* puts it this way: "And this love which God blesses is intended to be fruitful and to be realized in the common work of watching over creation" (CCC 1604). Father and mother watch over, support, provide for, and shepherd their children to prepare them for adult life and an eternity in Heaven. Therefore, anything that intentionally interrupts or prevents this natural fruit of marriage is contrary to God's design and is seriously sinful. Some spouses are unable to have children, but this does not mean that their marriage cannot be fruitful. They are called to bear fruit in their union in other ways, such as through adoption, or devoting their lives to serving others.

The Graces of Marriage

Directions: Read the essay, then answer the questions that follow.

Jesus took the natural relationship of marriage and elevated that relationship to the level of a Sacrament. The Sacrament of Holy Matrimony forges an indissoluble bond between the husband and the wife that endures until the death of one of the spouses. We have learned that sacrifice is a requirement of Christian discipleship, and perhaps nowhere is this requirement more clear than in marriage. Spouses must choose, every single day of their lives, to put each other's needs ahead of their own. But, as always, Jesus does not leave the spouses to do this alone. Indeed, on their own they would not be capable of the love God intends for us in marriage.

The Wedding at Cana, by Paolo Veronese

Marriage and Virtue

All the virtues are given life by charity (love). The theological virtue of charity, which we receive in Baptism, upholds and purifies our human ability to love and raises it to the supernatural perfection of divine love. In other words, the virtue of charity perfects our human love and makes it mirror the Divine Love that is God. "The *fruits* of charity are joy, peace, and mercy" (CCC 1829). In a marriage rooted in virtue, the spouses and their children are joyful, at peace, and merciful to one another, ultimately reflecting with each other God's love for us.

The Graces of Marriage

In this Sacrament, one man and one woman who are baptized are united by Christ Himself so that the two become one flesh. This happens when the spouses, usually in the context of the Nuptial Mass, express their consent before the priest or deacon in church, swear their vows to each other before God, and exchange rings as a sign of their covenantal bond. In Holy Matrimony the husband and wife are the actual ministers of the Sacrament.

The Sacrament of Holy Matrimony forges an indissoluble bond that endures till death. It is indissoluble because God Himself makes the bond. When God does something, we do not have the power to undo it. For example, once a person is baptized, he cannot "undo" the baptismal seal upon his soul, even if he decides to stop practicing the Faith. Jesus said about spouses in the Gospel of Matthew: "So they are no longer two, but one flesh. Therefore, what God has joined together, no human being must separate" (Matthew 19:6).

Ultimately, marriage requires sacrifice and, very often, endurance in suffering. The graces the spouses receive perfect their love and make it more like Christ's. As Christ sanctifies us, husband and wife help each other become holy and get to Heaven. And the love, peace, and joy experienced by the spouses in a sacramental marriage offer a glimpse of that which awaits them in Heaven.

1. What type of bond is formed between the spouses in a sacramental marriage?
   a indissoluble bond

2. How long does this bond endure? _until death_

3. What are the fruits of the theological virtue of charity (love)?
   Joy, peace, and mercy

4. Why can't the bond of marriage be undone?
   Because God himself seals, and makes the bond

Reflection Question

Jesus said that whoever wishes to come after Him must deny himself and "take up his cross" (Matthew 16:24). With this in mind, how do spouses help each other on the path of Christian discipleship?

Because when people

Holy Matrimony Graphic Organizer

Directions: Use information from this guide, your class notes, and the *Catechism of the Catholic Church* nos. 1601-1666 to complete 1-5 on this chart. Share your personal reflections for 6-7.

1 Scriptural basis of this Sacrament.	
2 Words spoken with this Sacrament (form).	
3 Things used or done when this Sacrament is received (matter).	marrage is based on the concent of the two spouces
4 Effects of this Sacrament.	To perfect the love the spouces have for one another
5 Ordinary minister of this Sacrament.	
6 How does this Sacrament reveal God's life-giving love?	
7 If you marry one day, how will this Sacrament help you to become more like your Heavenly Father?	

Sophia SketchPad Reflection Questions

Directions: After watching and discussing the video, explain any *new* insights you gained about why each of the following statements is true.

1. Marriage is a reflection of the Divine Love that is God, who is Trinity, Father, Son, and Holy Spirit.

    _____

    _____

2. God's love is an unbreakable bond of life-giving love that man and woman share in when they join together in marriage.

    _____

    _____

3. A loving home with a father and a mother is the model chosen by the Lord and therefore the ideal environment in which to raise a child.

    _____

    _____

    _____

4. Sin weakens husbands and wives by promoting selfishness, which damages their ability to love one another.

_____

_____

_____

5. The state of marriage in our world today does not reflect how God intended it to be.

_____

_____

_____

6. Jesus suffered and died on the Cross to save us from sin – and all of its effects, which includes the effects of sin on marriage.

_____

_____

_____

Holy Orders Pre-Assessment

Directions: In the left-hand column mark each statement true or false. Mark them again in the right column at the end of our study of Holy Orders to see if you were right.

Before beginning your study

At the end of your study

True or False?   **Statement**   **True or False?**

_____ 1. Jesus made St. Peter the head of His Church on earth. _____

_____ 2. Catholics worship the pope and believe he is sinless. _____

_____ 3. The Sacrament of Holy Orders forgives sin and gives us an "order of penance" to perform. _____

_____ 4. At the Last Supper, Jesus made the Apostles the first priests. _____

_____ 5. Jesus commanded the Apostles to celebrate Holy Mass for all Christians. _____

_____ 6. The fact that only men can be ordained to the priesthood shows that the Catholic Church thinks women are inferior. _____

_____ 7. The Sacrament of Holy Orders includes three degrees: deacon, priest, bishop. _____

_____ 8. The Church offers the priesthood to all men who perform 500 hours of service to the poor and successfully pass a written exam. _____

The Miraculous Draught of Fishes
BY JACOPO BASSANO (1545)

National Gallery of Art, Washington, Patrons' Permanent Fund 1997.21.1.

286

The Miraculous Draught of Fishes

The Miraculous Draught of Fishes, by Jacopo Bassano (1545)

Directions: Before beginning any analysis, take some time to quietly view and reflect on the art. During this time, don't worry about understanding anything in an intellectual way. Let yourself be inspired in any way that happens naturally. Then take some time to think about the questions below, and discuss them with your classmates.

1. Who are the people in this painting?

2. Look at the posture of the disciples. The two closest to Christ are Peter (kneeling) and Andrew (striding toward Him). What does Peter's body language seem to say? Andrew's?

3. Read Luke 5:1–11. How does this passage help you understand this scene?

4. In the Gospel account of this scene, Jesus instructs His disciples to "put out into the deep." What was Jesus teaching them about their mission?

5. Explain two things Peter did in response to Christ's command. From what you already know, how do these actions relate to the Sacrament of Holy Orders?

6. Jesus said to Peter and Andrew, "Come after me, and I will make you fishers of men" (Matthew 4:19). What did He mean?

7. Bishops and priests are successors of the Apostles. How are they like "fishers of men"?

8. The painting is titled *The Miraculous Draught of Fishes*. What miracle has Jesus performed in this Gospel story? What does Jesus' miracle teach the disciples about their work as "fishers of men"?

The Story of Holy Orders

Directions: Read the essay, then answer the questions that follow.

Holy Orders is the Sacrament through which Christ continues His ministry in the Church until the end of time. At the Last Supper, Jesus made the Apostles the first priests, commanding them to celebrate Mass for all Christians. He gave priests other spiritual powers so that all people everywhere would be able to encounter Jesus here on earth through the Sacraments. The Sacrament of Holy Orders includes three degrees: deacon, priest, bishop.

The story of the priesthood

The priesthood is a great mystery of faith revealed to us by Jesus Christ, who is the only true priest. His priesthood was prefigured in the Old Testament by the Levitical priesthood and by the mysterious priesthood of Melchizedek. Because Jesus is fully God and fully man, He established the new and definitive priesthood in which He is both the Priest offering and the Victim being offered for the forgiveness of sins, ours and those of the whole world.

Every baptized member of Christ participates in the priesthood of Christ as a prophet, priest, and king, joining the Lord Jesus in preaching and teaching (prophet), in sanctifying (priest), and in guiding others to Him (king) according to his or her vocation in the Church. This type of priesthood is called the "common priesthood" of the baptized.

Jesus did something special, however, when He established the Sacrament of Holy Orders.

Out of all His disciples, Jesus chose twelve men to be His Apostles. Beginning with these twelve men, He chose and consecrated certain men from the ranks of the baptized who would share in His priesthood in a unique way. Although all Christians should strive to be Christ-like, bishops and priests, by virtue of the Sacrament of Holy Orders, are called to be like Christ in a special way. They are consecrated – that is, set apart in a sacred way – to serve *in persona Christi Capitis* (in the person of Christ the Head).

Peter the rock

Christ knew that He would die on the Cross to save mankind and that He would establish a Church to carry on His work until the end of time. He commissioned Peter with the responsibility of the Keys of the Kingdom, to be first among the Apostles and thus become the first Pope: "Simon Peter said in reply, 'You are the Messiah, the Son of the living God.' Jesus said to him in reply, 'Blessed are you, Simon son of Jonah. For flesh and blood has not revealed this to you, but my heavenly Father. And so I say to you, you are Peter, and upon this rock I will build my church, and the gates of the netherworld shall not prevail against it. I will give you the keys to the kingdom of heaven. Whatever you bind on earth shall be bound in heaven; and whatever you loose on earth shall be loosed in heaven'" (Matthew 16:16-19). Jesus gave Peter the authority to make decisions that would be binding on earth and in Heaven. In other words, our Lord gave Peter authority to head the Church on earth.

The Last Supper

The heart of Christ's commands to the Apostles came at the first Holy Mass: the Last Supper. Before the Passover feast began, Jesus demonstrated how they were supposed to lead His flock—by loving them to the end. He got up from the table and washed their feet. He said, "I have given you a model to follow, so that as I have done for you, you should also do" (John 13:15). This act, like all of Jesus' acts, was one of love. He did it to give an example of the kind of humble, self-giving love that priests—and all Christians—should show one another. The washing of the Apostles' feet

gave form to His new commandment: "I give you a new commandment: love one another. As I have loved you, so you also should love one another. This is how all will know that you are my disciples, if you have love for one another" (John 13:34-35).

Finally, Christ commanded His Apostles to offer His saving sacrifice in the Holy Eucharist: "Then he took the bread, said the blessing, broke it, and gave it to them, saying, 'This is my body, which will be given for you; do this in memory of me'" (Luke 22:19). Every time a bishop or a priest consecrates the bread and wine at Holy Mass, it becomes the Body and Blood of Christ, and the bishop or priest is following Christ's command at the Last Supper.

1. Who is the one true priest? _Jesus_

2. Jesus calls every one of us to holiness. But how was Jesus' call to the Apostles special?
Because they are set apart to serve

3. What is the meaning of *in persona Christi Capitis*? _In the person of christ the head_

4. What is the significance of Jesus' words to St. Peter in Matthew 16:16-19?
He gave Peter the keys of the church.

5. What is the New Commandment? How does it connect to the Sacrament of Holy Orders?
To love one another. Because everything Jesus does is out of love.

Reflection Question

On your own paper, write what you think is the most important command Christ gave to the Apostles and why.

Holy Orders in Sacred Scripture

Directions: Read the information, then fill in the chart using your Bible.

Jesus is the Good Shepherd and the one true Priest. The mission of bishops and priests is to be *pastors* (from the Latin pastor, or "shepherd"), faithfully exercising the sacred powers received from Christ Himself of teaching, sanctifying, and shepherding Christ's flock on earth. Both Sacred Scripture and Sacred Tradition can help us to understand the Sacrament through which Christ continues His ministry in the Church until the end of time.

Summarize the Scripture passage	How does this verse relate to Holy Orders?
1 Genesis 14:18:	
2 John 20:21-23:	
3 Acts 6:1-6:	

Summarize the Scripture passage	How does this verse relate to Holy Orders?
4 Acts 13:3:	
5 1 Timothy 3:1:	
6 1 Timothy 4:14:	
7 2 Timothy 1:6:	
8 Titus 1:5:	

The Ministerial Priesthood

Directions: Read the essay, then discuss the questions that follow.

The Sacrament of Holy Orders has three degrees: bishop, priest and deacon. Bishops, the successors of the Apostles, have the fullness of the Sacrament of Holy Orders and the fullness of Christ's sacred powers and authority. Priests are consecrated as the primary collaborators with the bishops and have many of the sacred powers and authority of Christ. You can see them exercising their sacred powers when they preach at Mass, teach in school, speak out against various injustices in society, advocate for the poor and the vulnerable, administer the Sacraments, hear Confessions, offer Holy Mass, bury the dead, and lead and govern the parish, helping to guide all people toward Heaven. Those in Holy Orders are to be true spiritual fathers to those entrusted to them and to give their lives for Christ's flock. Deacons are consecrated primarily in service to the poor and have some of Christ's sacred powers and authority to preach, baptize, witness marriages, and bury the dead.

The ministerial priesthood

The type of priesthood Jesus established in the Sacrament of Holy Orders by setting apart and consecrating His Twelve Apostles to act *in persona Christi Capitis* is called the "ministerial priesthood."

Those consecrated in this Sacrament share in the priesthood of Christ in a very distinguished way. Like the Apostles, these men do not preach, sanctify, and govern by their own authority. The authority that bishops and priests are given to act in the person of Christ, the Head of the Church, comes from Jesus Himself. He gives them His very own sacred powers. He consecrates them as He did His first Apostles to preach and teach, to sanctify, and to govern the Mystical Body of Christ, the Church.

After His Death and Resurrection, Jesus spoke to the Apostles and sent them forth as God the Father had sent Him: "'Peace be with you. As the Father has sent me, so I send you.' And when he had said this, he breathed on them and said to them, 'Receive the holy Spirit. Whose sins you forgive are forgiven them, and whose sins you retain are retained'" (John 20:21-23).

St. Paul tells us how Jesus' sacred authority is passed on to those men who would follow in the line of the Apostles. St. Paul wrote to St. Timothy, "I remind you to stir into flame the gift of God that you have through the imposition of my hands" (2 Timothy 1:6).

Why only men?

God created man and woman in His own image and likeness. Moreover, we are all equally saved by faith in Jesus Christ and Baptism. St. Paul wrote to the Galatians, saying, "Through faith you are all children of God in Christ Jesus. For all of you who were baptized into Christ have clothed yourselves with Christ. There is neither Jew nor Greek, there is neither slave nor free person, there is not male and female; for you are all one in Christ Jesus" (Galatians 3:26-28). All people baptized into Christ equally share in His promise of salvation and are members of His Mystical Body, the Church.

This God-given fundamental equality between man and woman is recognized by civil government. For example, the founding fathers of the United States, in the Declaration of Independence, write that human beings are all created equal and are all endowed by their Creator with certain inalienable rights, such as life, liberty, and the pursuit of happiness. As citizens of the United States we have the right to own property, to vote, to open a business, to petition the government, to bear arms, to gather publicly, to run for political office, and so forth.

With all this in mind, it is important to remember that no one has a right to the Sacraments. The seven Sacraments were established by Jesus Himself to impart His divine life to us through visible signs. They are His gift to His Bride, the Church. No one has a "right" to any Sacrament, including Holy Orders. The Sacrament of Holy Orders is not given because of talent or achievement or because it is earned. It is given to those whom Jesus has chosen through His Church. Since the Sacraments have been established by Christ Himself, the Church is not free to change their essence. Rather the Church faithfully hands on what she received from Christ—water for Baptism, bread and wine for the Holy Eucharist, and so forth.

This concept of Sacraments as "gifts" rather than "rights" can be hard to understand, as we are so used to the idea that we can attain whatever we want with hard work and the

right attitude. But if you think about it, it might not seem so odd. Creatures have a nature. No matter how hard you worked, you could never fly like a bird or breathe under water like a fish. No matter how hard a man tried, he could never give birth to a baby. We see in Creation that God created man and woman in His own image and likeness, but He also made them different. They are equal in dignity and complementary in mission. The differences between man and woman do not indicate inequality but complementarity—man and woman were made for each other. The differences between them were to create loving communion. God gifted man and woman differently so that they could give to each other uniquely. Man cannot be woman, and woman cannot be man. This is true for our souls and body, and this truth is written even in our DNA.

So whom did Jesus choose as His Apostles? He could have chosen anyone, first because He is God and second because often in the Scriptures He was not bound by the conventions of the time, especially in the way He treated women. They were His most faithful followers, especially during His Passion, when all but one of His Apostles had fled. Jesus chose men as His Twelve Apostles, the first to receive the Sacrament of Holy Orders. So those who would follow in their line (apostolic succession) would be men, faithfully following what Christ Himself had established. We can see one of the reasons He called only men to serve in Holy Orders in that this Sacrament reveals Jesus' relationship to His Bride, the Church. He is the Head of the Church and her Husband. The Apostles were called to sacramentalize that reality. To act *in persona Christi Capitis* means to act as a husband to the Church and become a spiritual father. This is why we can truly call priests "Father."

We can see that Jesus' choice of only men to serve as Apostles does not mean that women are somehow inferior, less talented, or unable to do the things that priests do. To be woman is to symbolize a different reality – namely, that of the Church, and to become mothers, biologically or spiritually. The Sacrament of Holy Orders is to perpetuate in the Church the reality of Jesus Christ, Head and Husband of the Church.

Conversation Questions

1. What is the ministerial priesthood?

2. Who are the successors of the Apostles? On whose authority do they preach, sanctify, and govern?

3. What are the three degrees of Holy Orders?

4. How do we know we all share the same, equal human dignity?

5. How do we know we are all equal under the law?

6. Do you have a right to any of the Sacraments? For example:

    a. Does a non-believing adult have a right to Baptism?

    b. Does a non-believing adult have a right to Confirmation?

    c. Does a non-believing adult have a right to receive the Eucharist?

    d. If you are not sorry for your sins, can you demand that a priest grant you absolution? If you do not really intend to do your assigned penance, do you have a right to forgiveness anyway?

7. How would it change the concept of a "Sacrament" if someone could demand it?

8. Should the Church "change with the times," or should the Church remain bound by the decisions Christ made?

Feed My Sheep

Directions: In the left space, write down personal qualities revealed about Jesus Christ in each passage. On the right, write down qualities this passage makes you think bishops and priests ought to have, based on the example of Christ.

Qualities of Jesus Christ		Qualities bishops/priests should have
Leadership qualities Patience	1. After [Jesus] had finished speaking, he said to Simon, "Put out into deep water and lower your nets for a catch." Simon said in reply, "Master, we have worked hard all night and have caught nothing, but at your command I will lower the nets." When they had done this, they caught a great number of fish and their nets were tearing. –LUKE 5:4-6	Leadership qualities
Cooperation and Partnership	2. They signaled to their partners in the other boat to come to help them. They came and filled both boats so that they were in danger of sinking. –LUKE 5:7	Teamwork
humility repentant	3. When Simon Peter saw this, he fell at the knees of Jesus and said, "Depart from me, Lord, for I am a sinful man." –LUKE 5:8	repentant humility

Qualities of Jesus Christ		Qualities bishops/priests should have
Trust	4. For astonishment at the catch of fish they had made seized him and all those with him, and likewise James and John, the sons of Zebedee, who were partners of Simon. Jesus said to Simon, "Do not be afraid; from now on you will be catching men." When they brought their boats to the shore, they left everything and followed him. -LUKE 5:9-11	Trust
Forgiveness	5. They said to [Jesus], "Teacher, this woman was caught in the very act of committing adultery. Now in the law, Moses commanded us to stone such women. So what do you say?" ... "Let the one among you who is without sin be the first to throw a stone at her." ...And in response, they went away one by one.... Then Jesus said, "Neither do I condemn you. Go, [and] from now on do not sin any more." -JOHN 8:4-11	Forgiveness

Qualities of Jesus Christ		Qualities bishops/priests should have
	6. He took a towel and tied it around his waist. Then he poured water into a basin and began to wash the disciples' feet and dry them with the towel around his waist. He came to Simon Peter, who said to him, "Master, are you going to wash my feet?" Jesus answered and said to him, "What I am doing, you do not understand now, but you will understand later." Peter said to him, "You will never wash my feet." Jesus answered him, "Unless I wash you, you will have no inheritance with me." –JOHN 13:4-8	
	7. When they had finished breakfast, Jesus said to Simon Peter, "Simon, son of John, do you love me more than these?" He said to him, "Yes, Lord, you know that I love you." He said to him, "Feed my lambs." He then said to him a second time, "Simon, son of John, do you love me?" He said to him, "Yes, Lord, you know that I love you." He said to him, "Tend my sheep." He said to him the third time, "Simon, son of John, do you love me?" Peter was distressed that he had said to him a third time, "Do you love me?" and he said to him, "Lord, you know everything; you know that I love you." [Jesus] said to him, "Feed my sheep." –JOHN 21:15-17	

Holy Orders Graphic Organizer

Directions: Use information from this guide, your class notes, and the *Catechism of the Catholic Church* nos. 1536-1600 to complete 1-5 on this chart. Share your personal reflections for 6-7.

1 Scriptural basis of this Sacrament.	
2 Words spoken with this Sacrament (form).	
3 Things used or done when this Sacrament is received (matter).	
4 Effects of this Sacrament.	
5 Ordinary minister of this Sacrament.	
6 How does this Sacrament reveal God's life-giving love?	

7 As a Sacrament at the service of communion, Holy Orders, like marriage, is directed at the salvation of others. How does this Sacrament help called men to become more like their Heavenly Father? How does it help the people in their flock?

UNIT 4

Prayer

In this unit, you will learn about...

> The meaning of prayer
> Prayer in Salvation History
> The Lord's Prayer
> Prayer to the Father, Son, and Holy Spirit, in communion with Mary
> The various ways of praying, including the liturgy, devotional prayer, and praying with Scripture
> The witness of prayer from Mary and the saints

Introduction

Prayer, the raising of one's mind and heart to God or asking good things of Him, is inseparable from the Christian life. Prayer begins when we respond to God's call with openness. In fact, it is God who first calls out to us, whether we know it or not. The life of prayer is revealed to us throughout Salvation History. It is seen in the relationships of prayer of all of the figures of the Old Testament and culminates in Jesus' own example of prayer. Jesus teaches us to boldly approach the Father in prayer and how to order our petitions to Him. The Our Father, also called the Lord's Prayer, brings us into communion with the Father and His Son, Jesus Christ. In fact, the Lord's Prayer encompasses everything that can and must be said to the Father. Mary is our model of prayer, and the saints of the Church also provide beautiful examples of prayer, as can people in our own lives and parishes.

While prayer isn't always easy, there are many ways to seek the Lord in prayer. The sources of prayer are the Word of God, the liturgy of the Church, and the theological virtues of faith, hope, and charity. Through the Tradition of the Church, the Holy Spirit in the Church teaches the People of God to pray, as well as how to pray. The Holy Spirit teaches the Church and reminds the Church of all that Jesus said. Ever ancient, and ever new, the Holy Spirit inspires new expressions of the same basic forms of prayer: blessing, petition, intercession, thanksgiving, and praise. There are different forms of prayer (vocal, meditative, and contemplative). We have the liturgy of the Church, and the various devotional prayers, and different schools of Christian spirituality that share in the living tradition of prayer and guide us in the spiritual life. God wants us to speak to Him about our joys and sorrows, the good things and the bad, and He wants us to be still and listen and rest in His presence. Prayer is above all a loving relationship with God. Praying to our Father in Heaven should make us want to be like Him, and, as His children, develop in us a humble and trusting heart.

Are there any questions you still have about the topics you learned last month? What steps can you take to find out the answers?

_____

_____

_____

_____

What questions do you have right now about the topics you will be learning about in this unit?

_____

_____

_____

_____

Unit 4 Vocabulary

Adoration: A form of prayer in which we worship God and express our love for Him. Also refers to the Adoration of the Blessed Sacrament. This is when a consecrated host, the Real Presence of Christ in the Eucharist, is placed in a vessel called a monstrance (which means "to show") and displayed for the faithful to worship. In this form of prayer with the Blessed Sacrament, the faithful express their love for Jesus, and contemplate the mystery of His presence.

Filial: The relationship of a son or daughter as to a parent. Jesus revealed God's Fatherly love for us. Therefore, we can boldly approach God as our Father, as Jesus taught us.

Lectio Divina: Latin for "divine reading." It is an ancient form of praying with Scripture that is a slow and thoughtful encounter with the Word of God.

Liturgy of the Hours: Also called the Divine Office, it is the public prayer of the Church which sanctifies the whole course of the day and night. It consists of a variety of prayers, Scripture readings, most especially the Psalms, and writings of the saints. It is divided into seven "hours" or "offices," each to be prayed at specific times of the day. Bishops, priests, deacons, and religious are obligated to pray the full sequence of the hours, observing as closely as possible the true time of day. Lay persons are also encouraged to pray the Liturgy of the Hours so that it may be the prayer of the whole People of God.

Mediatrix of Grace: Title for Mary that describes her instrumental role in our salvation as the Mother of God. Her "yes" to God allowed God's plan for salvation to be completed in His Son, Jesus Christ. Therefore, she acted as a mediator (mediatrix), or go between, of God's grace. As Queen of Heaven, Mary continues to mediate all graces that come to us by her son, Jesus Christ. Mary's unique cooperation with her son in no way diminishes His own mediation, but flows from it, depends entirely on it, and draws all its power from it.

Meditation: A form of prayer in which we engage our minds and hearts in reflection on God and the things of God, often using spiritual readings from Scripture.

Novena: A nine-day prayer for a specific intention.

Pilgrimage: Prayerful journeys to holy places, such as the Holy Land, a site of an apparition of Mary, or even to a holy place in one's own diocese.

Prayer: Raising one's mind and heart to God in praise of His glory, asking for some desired good, giving Him thanks, or asking for His blessing on others. Through a life of prayer we experience a relationship with God.

Psalm: One of 150 songs, poems, and prayers found in the Book of Psalms in the Old Testament. They have been used in prayer since the time of the ancient Jews and continue to be prayed with at Mass, in the Liturgy of the Hours, and in other forms of prayer. It is believed that King David wrote around half of them. Many are originally songs or hymns meant to be sung in liturgical settings. There are different types of psalms, which include hymns, psalms of lament or sorrow, psalms of thanksgiving, royal psalms which praise the reigning king, and wisdom psalms which help us understand the ways of the Lord.

Relic: An artifact of the saints and their holy lives worthy of veneration, such as their bodies, something they owned, or other items closely associated with them. While a relic does not give us grace directly, we believe they can be vessels for grace that bring us closer in relationship to God.

Rosary: A special prayer in which we reflect on the Joyful, Sorrowful, Luminous, and Glorious Mysteries – important events in the lives of Jesus and Mary. Using a chain of beads, we make the Sign of the Cross and recite the Apostles' Creed while holding the crucifix; then we pray one Our Father, three Hail Mary's, and a Glory Be. Next, we recite the Our Father on each large bead, the Hail Mary on each of the ten smaller beads, and finish with the Glory Be. That completes one decade. Before we begin each decade, we say the mystery for that decade and think about it as we pray the prayers. After five decades, we pray the Hail Holy Queen and make the Sign of the Cross.

Spouse of the Holy Spirit: Title for Mary that describes her close relationship with the Holy Spirit. Mary became the Mother of God by the power of the Holy Spirit.

Stations of the Cross: A traditional devotional prayer that focuses on the Passion of Jesus. It follows Jesus' path as He carried His Cross and was crucified. Most parishes have a series of plaques, icons, or other works of art that present the 14 stations for devotion, meditation, and prayer.

Types of Prayer: Various forms of prayer developed in the great liturgical and spiritual traditions of the Church which include blessing and adoration, petition, intercession, thanksgiving, and praise.

Veneration: The act of honoring. As Catholics we honor the saints and other artifacts of their holy lives, called relics.

Visitation: The Gospel story of Mary's visit to her cousin Elizabeth shortly after the Angel Gabriel had appeared to Mary to announce the Incarnation. At their meeting, the child in Elizabeth's womb, John the Baptist, leapt for joy in the presence of the unborn Jesus.

The Miraculous Draught of Fishes

BY JACOPO BASSANO (1545)

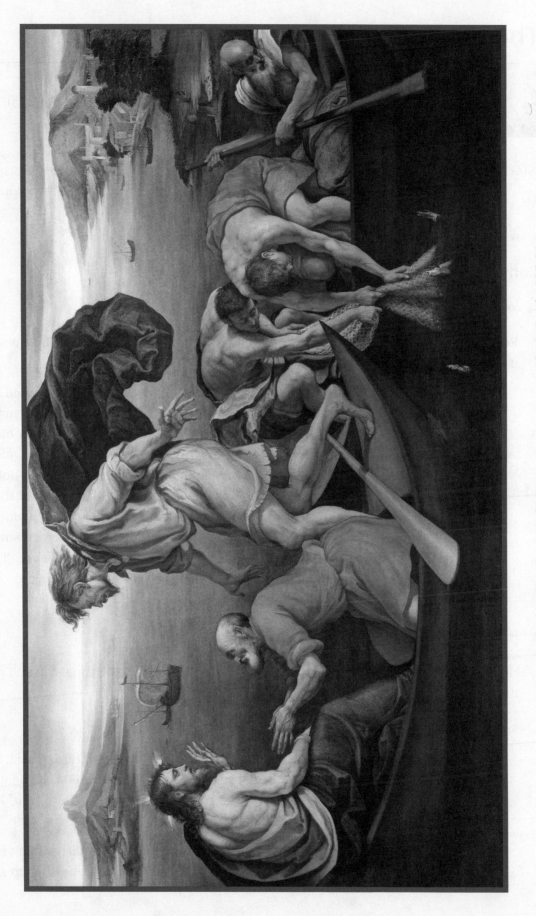

National Gallery of Art, Washington, Patrons' Permanent Fund 1997.21.1

The Miraculous Draught of Fishes

The Miraculous Draught of Fishes, *by Jacopo Bassano (1545)*

Directions: Take some time to quietly view and reflect on the art. Let yourself be inspired in any way that happens naturally. Then think about the questions below, and discuss them with your classmates.

Conversation Questions

1. Who is in this picture? How does each person seem to be feeling?

2. Read Luke 5:4-11. Did Simon, James, and John recognize that it was Jesus who caused the miraculous draught of fishes?

> After he had finished speaking, he said to Simon, "Put out into deep water and lower your nets for a catch." Simon said in reply, "Master, we have worked hard all night and have caught nothing, but at your command I will lower the nets." When they had done this, they caught a great number of fish and their nets were tearing. They signaled to their partners in the other boat to come to help them. They came and filled both boats so that they were in danger of sinking. When Simon Peter saw this, he fell at the knees of Jesus and said, "Depart from me, Lord, for I am a sinful man." For astonishment at the catch of fish they had made seized him and all those with him, and likewise James and John, the sons of Zebedee, who were partners of Simon. Jesus said to Simon, "Do not be afraid; from now on you will be catching men." When they brought their boats to the shore, they left everything and followed him.

3. How did they each react?

4. How would you describe Peter's feelings and attitude, based on the things he said and did in this passage?

5. Read 1 Samuel 3:4-10, 19-21. How did Samuel react at first to the Lord's call?

> The LORD called to Samuel, who answered, "Here I am." He ran to Eli and said, "Here I am. You called me." "I did not call you," Eli answered. "Go back to sleep." So he went back to sleep. Again the LORD called Samuel, who rose and went to Eli. "Here I am," he said. "You called me." But he answered, "I did not call you, my son. Go back to sleep."
>
> Samuel did not yet recognize the LORD, since the word of the LORD had not yet been revealed to him. The LORD called Samuel again, for the third time. Getting up and going

to Eli, he said, "Here I am. You called me." Then Eli understood that the LORD was calling the youth. So he said to Samuel, "Go to sleep, and if you are called, reply, 'Speak, LORD, for your servant is listening.'" When Samuel went to sleep in his place, the LORD came and stood there, calling out as before: Samuel, Samuel! Samuel answered, "Speak, for your servant is listening."

Samuel grew up, and the LORD was with him, not permitting any word of his to go unfulfilled. Thus all Israel from Dan to Beer-sheba came to know that Samuel was a trustworthy prophet of the LORD. The LORD continued to appear at Shiloh, manifesting himself to Samuel at Shiloh through his word. Samuel's word spread throughout Israel.

6. How did Samuel react the fourth time the Lord called to him?

7. How would you describe Samuel's feelings and attitude, based on the things he said and did in this passage?

8. In both of these passages, who initiates the conversation? What does this teach us about how all prayer begins?

9. The *Catechism* tells us that prayer is the raising of one's mind and heart to God or the requesting of good things from God. Does this painting show people raising their minds and heart to God, or requesting good things from God, or both? Explain.

Brainstorming About Prayer

Directions: Write what Samuel and Peter did before, during, and after their conversations with God.

Before

During

After

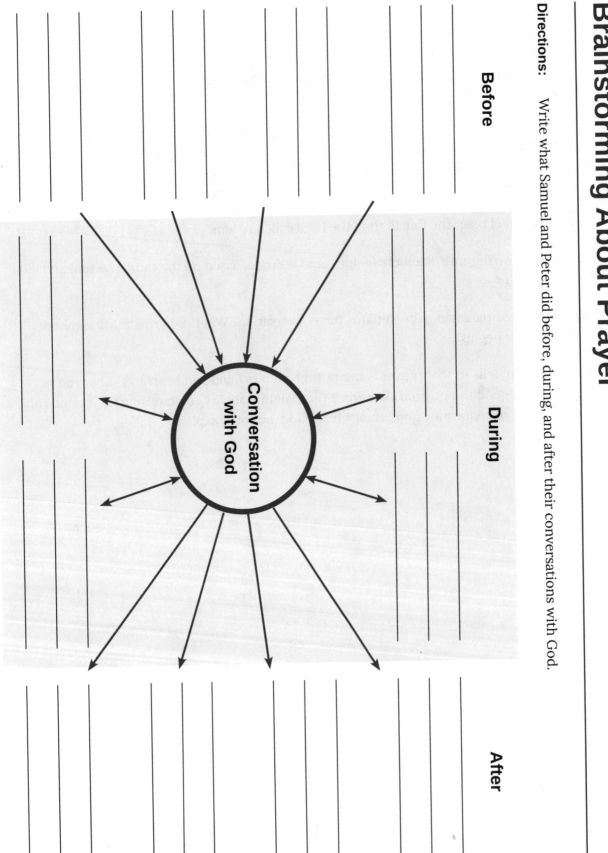

Conversation with God

UNIT 4, LESSON 1

Growing in Prayer

Directions: Read and/or listen to the following quotations and reflect on how you can apply them in your own life. Then thoughtfully and prayerfully answer the questions below.

St. Thérèse of Liseux, quoted in CCC 2258

"For me, prayer is a surge of the heart; it is a simple look turned toward heaven, it is a cry of recognition and of love, embracing both trial and joy."

CCC 2559

"Only when we humbly acknowledge that 'we do not know how to pray as we ought,' are we ready to receive freely the gift of prayer. 'Man is a beggar before God.'"

CCC 2560

"Whether we realize it or not, prayer is the encounter of God's thirst with ours. God thirsts that we may thirst for him."

CCC 2561

"Prayer is the response of faith to the free promise of salvation and also a response of love to the thirst of the only Son of God."

CCC 2562-2563

"According to Scripture, it is the *heart* that prays. If our heart is far from God, the words of prayer are in vain. ...The heart is our hidden center, beyond the grasp of our reason and of others; only the Spirit of God can fathom the human heart and know it fully. The heart is the place of decision, deeper than our psychic drives. It is the place of truth, where we choose life or death. It is the place of encounter, because as image of God we live in relation: it is the place of covenant."

CCC 2564

"Christian prayer is a covenant relationship between God and man in Christ. It is the action of God and of man, springing forth from both the Holy Spirit and ourselves, wholly directed to the Father, in union with the human will of the Son of God made man."

CCC 2565

"In the New Covenant, prayer is the living relationship of the children of God with their Father who is good beyond measure, with his Son Jesus Christ and with the Holy Spirit."

CCC 2565

"The life of prayer is the habit of being in the presence of the thrice-holy God and in communion with him."

1. Which passage from the *Catechism* stands out most to you? Why?

   _____

   _____

2. What new habits can you cultivate, or what old habits can you improve, to act on the teaching of this passage in your life?

   _____

   _____

3. How do Samuel and/or St. Peter give you examples of how you can grow closer to God through prayer?

   _____

   _____

4. We can sometimes feel like we are "too busy" to pray. From all you have read and learned, is prayer something "extra" we should try to do from time to time, or is it fundamental to the Christian life? Explain.

   _____

   _____

   _____

   _____

1 Samuel 3:10

The LORD came and stood there, calling out as before: Samuel, Samuel! Samuel answered, "Speak, for your servant is listening."

Mark 11:24

Therefore I tell you, all that you ask for in prayer, believe that you will receive it and it shall be yours.

Luke 11:10

For everyone who asks, receives; and the one who seeks, finds; and to the one who knocks, the door will be opened.

Jeremiah 33:3

Call to me, and I will answer you; I will tell you great things beyond the reach of your knowledge.

_____

_____

_____

_____

_____

_____

_____

_____

_____

Luke 1:38

Mary said, "Behold, I am the handmaid of the Lord. May it be done to me according to your word."

_____

_____

_____

_____

_____

_____

_____

_____

1 Thessalonians 5:17

Pray without ceasing.

_____

_____

_____

_____

_____

_____

_____

_____

Hebrews 4:12

Indeed, the word of God is living and effective, sharper than any two-edged sword, penetrating even between soul and spirit, joints and marrow, and able to discern reflections and thoughts of the heart.

_____

_____

_____

_____

_____

_____

_____

_____

_____

_____

Luke 1:46-47

And Mary said: "My soul proclaims the greatness of the Lord; my spirit rejoices in God my savior."

Prayer Reflection

Directions: Follow along with the prayer reflection steps below. Take the time to pray and reflect before writing your responses to the reflection questions.

Steps

➤ Begin with the Sign of the Cross. Remember that you are in the presence of God. He is always with us. He is always waiting to hear our prayers.

➤ Close your eyes and imagine Christ on the Cross. This is where He demonstrated His everlasting love for us. Take some time to put yourself on that hill of Calvary. Pay attention to what you see and hear. Who is there? What is the atmosphere like?

➤ Take some time to think of all the things that worry you. Bring these worries, one by one, to the feet of Jesus on the Cross. Whether big or small, God can take care of these worries. Let them fade away slowly as you give them up to the Lord.

➤ Take some time to think of all the people who need your prayers. Bring these intentions, one by one, to the feet of Jesus on the Cross. Whether these intentions are big or small, God already knows them, and He has a plan for the good of His people.

➤ Take some time to think of all that you are grateful for. Thank Jesus for each of these things. Whether each is big or small, your family or the clothes on your back, bring these to the Lord with a grateful heart. Your gratitude consoles Jesus' Sacred Heart on the Cross.

➤ Take a deep breath and simply thank God for your life and for this day.

➤ Take some time to call upon the intercession of the saints and the angels. If you have a favorite saint or angel, you may ask for his or her intercession. For example, "Pope St. John Paul II and St. Michael the Archangel, pray for us." Or you may ask for the intercession of all the saints by praying something like, "All you holy men and women, pray for us."

➤ Conclude your time of prayer with a Hail Mary or a Glory Be and the Sign of the Cross.

Reflection

1. How did it feel to slow down and take time for prayer?

   _____

   _____

   _____

2. Was it easy or difficult to eliminate distractions and simply focus on God's presence? Why?

   _____

   _____

   _____

3. Was it easy for you to picture the scene that was described? Explain.

   _____

   _____

   _____

4. What is one thing that you were surprised about during your time of prayer?

   _____

   _____

   _____

5. How can you incorporate prayer time like this into every day?

   _____

   _____

   _____

Types of Prayer

Directions: Read the definitions of each type of prayer, and then write an example of each. You may use your class notes for reference.

1. **Blessing and Adoration:** Because God blesses our human hearts, our hearts can bless Him in return as the source of every blessing. Blessing and adoration is man's response to God's gift. We bless Him for having blessed us.

    _____

    _____

    _____

2. **Petition:** Petition is a prayer of asking for our needs.

    _____

    _____

    _____

3. **Intercession:** Intercession is prayer for others.

    _____

    _____

    _____

4. **Thanksgiving:** Prayer of thanksgiving is just that – thanking God for all that He is and all He has given us.

    _____

    _____

    _____

5. **Praise:** Praise recognizes that God is God and we are His children

    _____

    _____

    _____

Prayer in the Old Testament

Directions: Read about prayer in the Old Testament, then answer the questions that follow.

God is always the initiator of His relationship with man. Our first response is prayer, communication with Him. We see this prayer rising throughout Salvation History, beginning all the way back to the time of Adam of Eve and continuing throughout the Old Testament.

Adam and Eve, our original parents, enjoyed a close personal relationship with God. God walked and talked with Adam and Eve in the Garden of Eden and directly interacted with them. Genesis tells us how God spoke to them, gave them commands, and cared for them. After Adam and Eve sinned, they "heard the sound of the LORD God walking about in the garden at the breezy time of the day," as if it was something they were used to hearing, and when they had hidden themselves from God, He called out to them, "Where are you?" (Genesis 3:8-9). The first relationship of prayer was the relationship of intimate friends who lived together in paradise.

In the story of Abraham, we see the focus of his heart upon the Lord. Abraham's prayer is expressed first in quiet and in action. Along his journey, at every stop, he built an altar to God. Only later does he speak his first prayer, so much like our own at times, questioning when God would answer his prayer. Even when tested by God, when he was asked to sacrifice his only son, Isaac, Abraham's faith remained true. Through it all, Abraham's faith in God gives us an example that even through trials and temptation, when we remain faithful to the Lord, He will hear our prayer and fulfill His promises to us.

Moses is an example of intercessory prayer. In His relationship with God and His people, Moses consistently communicates the needs of the Israelites to God and prays on their behalf, even when they reject God. With Moses, we are reminded that the relationship of prayer always begins with God's initiative. In the story of the "burning bush" God called to Moses, who answered and followed His Word. The book of Exodus tells us "The LORD used to speak to Moses face to face, as a person speaks to a friend" (33:11). In his regular and lengthy conversation with God, we find a rich life of prayer that strengthened Moses and humbled him for his mission.

David is known in the Old Testament as the King "after [God's] own heart" (1 Samuel 13:14). He is the shepherd who prays for his people and prays in their name. Throughout his life David devoted himself to praising God and repenting when he failed. He became a model of prayer for the people of God. David was inspired by the Holy Spirit to write the psalms, which are songs of praise and thanksgiving, lamentation, and liturgy that speak of the human heart in prayer. They recall both the saving events of the past and future salvation through the Messiah.

Elijah is the "father" of the prophets and can also teach us about prayer. The mission of the prophets was to educate God's people in the faith and stir up a conversion of the heart. It is through the prophets' encounter with God that we see how to draw strength and light for the mission that He has for us. The one- on-one prayer of the prophets teaches us not to flee the challenges of this world but, rather, to be attentive to the Word of God in the world in anticipation of salvation.

1. In the relationship between God and man, who is always the initiator? What is the first response?

   _____

   _____

2. What sort of relationship with God did Adam and Eve enjoy?

   _____

   _____

   _____

3. How can the first relationship of prayer be described?

   _____

   _____

   _____

4. Where is Abraham's heart focused?

   _____

5. How is Abraham's prayer first expressed? What does Abraham build at every stop along his journey?

   _____

6. What is Abraham's first spoken prayer?

   _____

7. What example does Abraham give us?

   _____

   _____

8. How is Moses an example of intercessory prayer?

_____

_____

9. How did God speak with Moses?

_____

10. What do we find in Moses' regular and lengthy conversations with God?

_____

_____

_____

11. What is David known as in the Old Testament? _____

_____

12. What did David devote himself to? _____

_____

13. What are the psalms? _____

_____

_____

14. What was the mission of the prophets?

_____

_____

15. What does the one-on-one prayer of the prophets teach us?

_____

_____

Seek and Knock

The Lord's Prayer, which Jesus gave us in His most important teaching, the Sermon on the Mount, can be considered a summary of the whole Gospel. In this prayer, and through His entire life, Jesus reveals God as our Father in Heaven. As with every vocal prayer, we shouldn't just repeat the words unthinkingly. Rather, we should turn our hearts towards God and remember that the Holy Spirit teaches us to pray through His Word. It is no accident that we say the Our Father at Mass between the Eucharistic Prayer and Holy Communion. It summarizes all that has come before, and as the *Catechism* puts it, "knocks at the door of the Banquet of the kingdom" that Holy Communion reminds us to look forward to (CCC 2770).

Directions: Read Matthew 7:7-11 and then answer the questions below in complete sentences.

Matthew 7:7-11

"Ask and it will be given to you; seek and you will find; knock and the door will be opened to you. For everyone who asks, receives; and the one who seeks, finds; and to the one who knocks, the door will be opened. Which one of you would hand his son a stone when he asks for a loaf of bread, or a snake when he asks for a fish? If you then, who are wicked, know how to give good gifts to your children, how much more will your heavenly Father give good things to those who ask him."

1. Who do you think is speaking in this passage? Why?

    _____

    _____

    _____

2. What does it mean to say, "Everyone who asks receives; and the one who seeks, finds; and to the one who knocks, the door will be opened"?

    _____

    _____

    _____

3. Why do you think Jesus gives the example of someone handing his son a stone or a snake?

_____

_____

_____

4. What does this passage teach us about prayer?

_____

_____

_____

5. Describe a time in your own life when you were reluctant to pray for something that you wanted or needed. What happened?

_____

_____

_____

_____

_____

_____

19th century steel engraving of Jesus Christ.

Parables of Prayer

Directions: Choose one of the three options. Then read that parable and on your own paper answer the questions for that option.

Option A

Luke 11:5-8

And he said to them, "Suppose one of you has a friend to whom he goes at midnight and says, 'Friend, lend me three loaves of bread, for a friend of mine has arrived at my house from a journey and I have nothing to offer him,' and he says in reply from within, 'Do not bother me; the door has already been locked and my children and I are already in bed. I cannot get up to give you anything.' I tell you, if he does not get up to give him the loaves because of their friendship, he will get up to give him whatever he needs because of his persistence.

1. Why did the friend come to the house?

2. What did Jesus say will be the response of the homeowner?

3. For what two reasons would the homeowner give his friend the bread?

4. What does this parable teach us about prayer?

5. What lesson can you learn from this parable about your own prayer life?

Option B

Luke 18:1-8

Then he told them a parable about the necessity for them to pray always without becoming weary. He said, "There was a judge in a certain town who neither feared God nor respected any human being. And a widow in that town used to come to him and say, 'Render a just decision for me against my adversary.' For a long time the judge was unwilling, but eventually he thought, 'While it is true that I neither fear God nor respect any human being, because this widow keeps bothering me I shall deliver a just decision for her lest she finally come and strike me.'" The Lord said, "Pay attention to what the dishonest judge says. Will not God then secure the rights of his chosen ones who call out to him day and night? Will he be slow to answer them? I tell you, he will see to it that justice is done for them speedily. But when the Son of Man comes, will he find faith on earth?"

1. Why did the widow come to the judge's house?

2. Why did the judge grant the widow what she asked of him?

3. Who is the "Son of Man"?

4. What does this parable teach us about prayer?

5. What lesson can you learn from this parable about your own prayer life?

Option C

Luke 18:9-14

He then addressed this parable to those who were convinced of their own righteousness and despised everyone else. "Two people went up to the temple area to pray; one was a Pharisee and the other was a tax collector. The Pharisee took up his position and spoke this prayer to himself, 'O God, I thank you that I am not like the rest of humanity—greedy, dishonest, adulterous—or even like this tax collector. I fast twice a week, and I pay tithes on my whole income.' But the tax collector stood off at a distance and would not even raise his eyes to heaven but beat his breast and prayed, 'O God, be merciful to me a sinner.' I tell you, the latter went home justified, not the former; for everyone who exalts himself will be humbled, and the one who humbles himself will be exalted."

1. To whom is Jesus speaking?

2. Who are the two characters in the story, and what was the difference in how they approached God and prayer?

3. Which one of these men was "justified," and why?

4. What does this parable teach us about prayer?

5. What lesson can you learn from this parable about your own prayer life?

The *Catechism* on Prayer

Directions: Read the following *Catechism* paragraph and then answer the questions below.

We learn to pray at certain moments by hearing the Word of the Lord and sharing in his Paschal mystery, but his Spirit is offered us at all times, in the events of *each day*, to make prayer spring up from us. Jesus' teaching about praying to our Father is in the same vein as his teaching about providence: time is in the Father's hands; it is in the present that we encounter him, not yesterday nor tomorrow, but today: "O that *today* you would hearken to his voice! Harden not your hearts." (CCC 2659)

1. How do we learn to pray at certain moments?

    _____

    _____

2. Jesus' teaching about praying to our Father is similar to His teaching about what?

    _____

    _____

3. Where/when do we encounter God?

    _____

    _____

4. What does it mean to "hearken" to God's voice and "harden not your hearts"?

    _____

    _____

5. How does this passage relate to your life? How can you incorporate these ideas into your own prayer?

    _____

    _____

God, Our Father

Directions: Watch the video, "ShareJesus Lent Video 23: God, Our Father" and then answer the questions below.

1. What, if anything, will remain with you about this video?

   _____

   _____

   _____

   _____

2. Alejandro asks, "What is *your* relationship with God?" Take a moment to think about this question and write your answer below.

   _____

   _____

   _____

   _____

   _____

   _____

   _____

   _____

   _____

The Lord's Prayer

Directions: The Lord's Prayer is the prayer that has the most to teach us about the Church. Read the Scripture passage, then answer the questions that follow.

This is how you are to pray: Our Father in heaven, hallowed be your name, your kingdom come, your will be done, on earth as in heaven. Give us today our daily bread; and forgive us our debts, as we forgive our debtors; and do not subject us to the final test, but deliver us from the evil one.

–MATTHEW 6:9-13

1. How does Christ say we are to address God?_____

2. Hallowed means greatly revered or respected; holy. So, what does it mean to say, "hallowed be your name"?

   _____

3. What condition is put on our own receiving of forgiveness?

   _____

4. What do we call the 2,000-year-old prayer that is based on Jesus' teaching here?

   _____

Reflection Questions

5. Put this teaching of Jesus' in context. When and where does He teach us the Lord's Prayer? Why is this setting important?

   _____

   _____

6. Remember the five types of prayer: blessing and adoration, petition, intercession, thanksgiving, and praise. Which type(s) of prayer is this?

   _____

The Our Father contains seven petitions. In the first three, we tell the Father that we long for His glory: we call His name holy (hallowed be thy name), we look forward to the coming of His Kingdom (thy Kingdom come), and we tell him that we want His will to be done (thy will be done, on earth as it is in Heaven). The four other petitions present our wants to the Father. We ask him to nourish our lives (give us this day, our daily bread), heal us from sin (forgive us our trespasses, as we forgive those who trespass against us), and to help us win the struggle of good over evil (and lead us not into temptation, but deliver us from evil.)

7. Pope St. John Paul II said, "Everything that can and must be said to the Father is contained in those seven requests which we all know by heart. There is such a simplicity in them that even a child can learn them, but at the same time such a depth that a whole life can be spent meditating on their meaning." Would you agree? Are there any prayers you have or could offer that do not fit within one of the petitions? Explain why or why not.

_____

_____

_____

_____

_____

_____

Lessons from Prayer

Directions: Read the Scripture passages, then answer the questions that follow.

Luke 5:15-16

The report about him spread all the more, and great crowds assembled to listen to him and to be cured of their ailments, but he would withdraw to deserted places to pray.

Matthew 6:5-7

When you pray, do not be like the hypocrites, who love to stand and pray in the synagogues and on street corners so that others may see them. ...But when you pray, go to your inner room, close the door, and pray to your Father in secret. ...In praying, do not babble like the pagans, who think that they will be heard because of their many words.

Mark 1:35

Rising very early before dawn, he left and went off to a deserted place, where he prayed.

Matthew 14:23

After doing so, he went up on the mountain by himself to pray. When it was evening he was there alone.

Luke 6:12

In those days he departed to the mountain to pray, and he spent the night in prayer to God.

1. What do all of these Scripture passages have in common?

   _____

2. Why do you think Jesus often went off by Himself to pray? What does this teach us? Did Jesus always pray alone, or did He ever pray in public?

   _____

   _____

   _____

3. What could be the benefit of rising early to pray?

   _____

   _____

4. The night before His Passion, Jesus prayed to the Father:

> Then Jesus came with them to a place called Gethsemane, and he said to his disciples, "Sit here while I go over there and pray." He took along Peter and the two sons of Zebedee, and began to feel sorrow and distress. Then he said to them, "My soul is sorrowful even to death. Remain here and keep watch with me." He advanced a little and fell prostrate in prayer, saying, "My Father, if it is possible, let this cup pass from me; yet, not as I will, but as you will." (Matthew 26:36-39)

Where is Jesus in this scene? How does Jesus feel during this time of prayer?

_____

_____

_____

5. What does Jesus ask of the Father? What does He mean by "let this cup pass from me"?

_____

_____

6. Explain a time when you have prayed in sorrow. Why were you sorrowful? What did you ask of God?

_____

_____

7. Recall our discussions about our filial relationship with the Father. What does this Scripture teach us about prayer and filial love?

_____

_____

_____

Our Lady of Guadalupe

332

Our Lady of Guadalupe

Directions: Look at the image of our Lady that appeared on St. Juan Diego's tilma and read the information. Then answer the questions that follow.

The Amazing Truth of Our Lady of Guadalupe

BY DAN LYNCH

Our Lady of Guadalupe appeared in Mexico as the pregnant Mother of God to Blessed Juan Diego, an Aztec Indian, on December 9, 10, and 12, 1531. She left a Miraculous Image of her appearance on his cactus fiber cloak, or "tilma", which still exists today for all to see in the Basilica of Our Lady of Guadalupe in Mexico City.

Our Lady came to offer faith, hope, and consolation to the oppressed natives of Mexico and to reconcile them with their Spanish rulers. She put an end to the bloody human sacrifice of the Aztecs and converted ten million natives in the next 10 years!

After the conquest, the Spanish rule of the natives was so severe that a bloody revolt was imminent. The bishop prayed for Our Lady to intervene to prevent an uprising, to reconcile the Spanish and the natives, and to bring peace. He asked that he would receive roses native to his homeland of Castile Spain as a sign that his prayer would be answered.

On December 9, 1531, Our Lady appeared to a recently converted Aztec named Juan Diego. She asked Juan Diego to go to the bishop and ask him to build a church for her on the barren hill of Tepeyac (which is now part of Mexico City). Our Lady wanted to show her merciful love to all of her children. The prudent bishop asked Juan to ask the Lady for a sign. Juan did so and Our Lady promised to give him the sign.

Three days later on December 12, Our Lady again appeared to Juan on Tepeyac Hill and told him to pick the Castilian roses that miraculously appeared there and bring them to the bishop as a sign for him to believe her request. Juan gathered the roses into his tilma (cloak) and brought them to the bishop.

He opened the tilma to show them and, to everyone's astonishment, the Image of Our Lady appeared on it. The bishop then built the church as Our Lady had requested, and ten million natives were converted and baptized in the one, true faith within the next 10 years.

Human sacrifice ended in Mexico forever. Our Lady of Guadalupe brought the light of the true faith, crushed the false gods of Mexico, and established an era of peace.

The image as pictograph

The Image of Our Lady is actually an Aztec pictograph that was read and understood quickly by the Aztec Indians.

THE LADY STOOD IN FRONT OF THE SUN – She was greater than their dreaded sun-god, Huitzilopochtli.

HER FOOT RESTED ON THE CRESCENT MOON – She had clearly vanquished their foremost deity, the feathered serpent Quetzalcoatl.

THE STARS STREWN ACROSS THE MANTLE – She was greater than the stars of heaven, which they worshiped. She was a virgin and the queen of the heavens, for Virgo rests over her womb and the northern crown upon her head. She appeared on December 12, 1531, and the stars that she wore are the constellation of stars that appeared in the sky that day!

THE BLUE-GREEN HUE OF HER MANTLE – She was a queen, for she wore the color of royalty.

THE BLACK CROSS ON THE BROOCH AT HER NECK – Her God was that of the Spanish Missionaries, Jesus Christ, her Son.

THE BLACK BELT – She was with child, for she wore the Aztec maternity belt.

THE FOUR-PETAL FLOWER OVER HER WOMB – She was the Mother of God. The flower was a special symbol of life, movement, and deity – the center of the universe.

HER HANDS ARE JOINED IN PRAYER – She was not God; clearly there was One greater than she, and she pointed her finger to the cross on her brooch.

THE DESIGN ON HER ROSE-COLORED GARMENT – She was the Queen of the Earth, for she wore a map of Mexico telling the Indians exactly where the apparition took place.

The image and science

The image to this date, cannot be explained by science.

The image shows no sign of deterioration after 450 years! The tilma, or cloak, of Juan Diego on which the image of Our Lady has been imprinted is a coarse fabric made from the threads of the maguey cactus. This fiber disintegrates within 20 to 60 years!

There is no under-sketch, no sizing, and no protective over-varnish on the image.

Microscopic examination revealed that there were no brush strokes.

The image seems to increase in size and change colors due to an unknown property of the surface and substance of which it is made.

According to Kodak of Mexico, the image is smooth and feels like a modern-day photograph. (It was produced 300 years before the invention of photography.)

The image has consistently defied exact reproduction, whether by brush or camera.

Several images can be seen reflected in the eyes of the Virgin. They are believed to be the images of Juan Diego, Bishop Juan de Zummaraga, Juan Gonzales, the interpreter, and others.

The distortion and place of the images are identical to what is produced in the normal eye, which is impossible to obtain on a flat surface.

The stars on Our Lady's mantle coincide with the constellation in the sky on December 12, 1531. All who have scientifically examined the image of Our Lady over the centuries confess that its properties are absolutely unique and so inexplicable in human terms that the image can only be supernatural!

This article is reprinted with permission from CatholicExchange.com.

1. What do you find most interesting or beautiful about this image of our Lady?

   _____

2. What do you find most interesting about the story of our Lady's appearances to St. Juan Deigo?

   _____

   _____

   _____

3. We read in the book of Revelation: "A great sign appeared in the sky, a woman clothed with the sun, with the moon under her feet, and on her head a crown of twelve stars" (12:1). How does this description connect to the image of Our Lady of Guadalupe?

   _____

   _____

   _____

4. According to author Fr. James Farfaglia, "Experts believe that the title Our Lady of Guadalupe came from a misunderstanding of the translation into Spanish of the Aztec word *coatlaxopeuh* or *Quatlasupe* [meaning "crusher of the serpent"]. Thus, Our Lady of Guadalupe is in reality Our Lady of Quatlasupe – "She who crushes the head of the serpent." Using Scripture, explain why this is significant.

   _____

   _____

   _____

   _____

5. Look at our Lady's posture in the image. How would you describe the way our Lady appears – triumphant or humble? Explain.

   _____

   _____

   _____

   _____

   _____

The Visitation

Directions: While she was carrying Jesus in her womb, Mary visited her cousin Elizabeth. Elizabeth was also pregnant at the time with her son, John the Baptist. We call this joyful event the Visitation. Read the Scripture passage and answer the following questions.

Luke 1:39-56

During those days Mary set out and traveled to the hill country in haste to a town of Judah, where she entered the house of Zechariah and greeted Elizabeth.

When Elizabeth heard Mary's greeting, the infant leaped in her womb, and Elizabeth, filled with the holy Spirit, cried out in a loud voice and said, "Most blessed are you among women, and blessed is the fruit of your womb. And how does this happen to me, that the mother of my Lord should come to me? For at the moment the sound of your greeting reached my ears, the infant in my womb leaped for joy. Blessed are you who believed that what was spoken to you by the Lord would be fulfilled."

And Mary said:

"My soul proclaims the greatness of the Lord; my spirit rejoices in God my savior. For he has looked upon his handmaid's lowliness; behold, from now on will all ages call me blessed. The Mighty One has done great things for me, and holy is his name. His mercy is from age to age to those who fear him. He has shown might with his arm, dispersed the arrogant of mind and heart. He has thrown down the rulers from their thrones but lifted up the lowly. The hungry he has filled with good things; the

Mary's Visit to Elizabeth, by Frans Francken the Younger.

rich he has sent away empty. He has helped Israel his servant, remembering his mercy, according to his promise to our fathers, to Abraham and to his descendants forever."

Mary remained with her about three months and then returned to her home.

1. What happened when Mary greeted her cousin?

   _____

2. Mary went to visit her cousin Elizabeth right after she learned she would be the mother of Jesus. She was only a few weeks pregnant at the time of the Visitation. How is it possible that Elizabeth and her baby both recognized Him?

   _____

   _____

3. "Blessed are you among women, and blessed is the fruit of your womb." Where have you heard these words before, and what do they mean?

   _____

   _____

4. In your own words, what is Mary's response to Elizabeth's exclamation and praise?

   _____

   _____

5. Recall the humble image of Our Lady of Guadalupe. Can you imagine her saying these words? Explain.

   _____

   _____

   _____

Mary at the Crucifixion

Directions: Read the Scripture passage, then answer the questions that follow in complete sentences.

John 19:25-27

Standing by the cross of Jesus were his mother and his mother's sister, Mary the wife of Clopas, and Mary of Magdala. When Jesus saw his mother and the disciple there whom he loved, he said to his mother, "Woman, behold, your son." Then he said to the disciple, "Behold, your mother." And from that hour the disciple took her into his home.

1. What do you think Mary was feeling as she watched her Son's Passion and Death?

   _____

2. Jesus was conceived in Mary's womb by the power of the Holy Spirit. Mary remained a virgin throughout her entire life. Why do you think Jesus chose to entrust His mother to His beloved disciple? Why does He tell His mother that St. John is her son?

   _____

   _____

3. Do Jesus' words "Behold your mother" have any meaning for us, His disciples?

   _____

   _____

4. What can we learn about prayer through Mary's presence at the foot of the Cross?

   _____

   _____

Mary and the Saints

Directions: Read the information and quotations below, then answer the questions at the end.

The Church gives Mary many titles, such as "Mother of God" and "Our Lady," which you have likely heard before. The Church also refers to Mary as the "Mediatrix" of grace. A mediator is one who serves as a go-between between two people or parties. The graces we receive from Jesus all come through the Blessed Virgin Mary: the God-bearer through whom the Savior entered the world. Mary's unique cooperation with her son in no way diminishes His own mediation, but flows from it, depends entirely on it, and draws all its power from it.

Mary was and is so close with the Holy Spirit, the Paraclete, that the title "Spouse of the Holy Spirit" is given to her to express this relationship. She was obedient to the Lord and close to Him in prayer, teaching us about trust and assent to God's will. Mary's will was (and is) so united to God's that we can say she is "conformed" to Him. This is true freedom in Christ, and it is our goal as well!

We ask for Mary's intercession to present our petitions to her Son. In other words, she brings our prayers to Jesus on our behalf. Mary does not replace Christ in any way, but she participates in our salvation in a very active way. Many saints in Church history had a special devotion to Our Lady, such as St. Louis de Montfort, St. Catherine Laboure, and Pope St. John Paul II.

St. Louis de Montfort, *True Devotion to Mary*

"Satan fears her not only more than angels and men but in a certain sense more than God himself. This does not mean that the anger, hatred and power of God are not infinitely greater than the Blessed Virgin's, since her attributes are limited. It simply means that Satan, being so proud, suffers infinitely more in being vanquished and punished by a lowly and humble servant of God, for her humility humiliates him more than the power of God. ...When the Holy Spirit, her spouse, finds Mary in a soul, he hastens there and enters fully into it. He gives himself generously to that soul according to the place it has given to his spouse" (52, 36).

St. Catherine Laboure

St. Catherine Laboure had a Miraculous Medal made after she was visited by Mary multiple times in her convent in France. Our Lady asked Catherine to have this medal made to spread devotion to the Immaculate Conception. When the medals were distributed, they eventually received the nickname, "Miraculous Medal," when many people came back with reports of prayers that were answered through the intercession of Our Lady.

Pope St. John Paul II

St. John Paul II was the Pope from 1978 to 2005. Many remember John Paul the Great for his beautiful devotion to our Blessed Mother. His papal motto was "Totus Tuus," meaning "totally yours," and his papal coat of arms contained a capital M beneath the Cross to symbolize his total consecration to Jesus through Mary. He considered Mary his mother and had a great devotion to praying the Rosary. He is one of the most beloved popes in all of Church history.

1. Which of these three saints do you find most interesting? Explain.

_____

_____

2. In your own words, explain what St. Louis de Montfort means when he speaks of how Satan "fears" Mary.

_____

_____

_____

3. In your own words, explain what St. Louis de Montfort means when he says that the Holy Spirit "gives himself" to souls where he finds Mary, His Spouse.

_____

_____

_____

Reflection

On your own paper and in your own words, write a short letter to God explaining what you have learned through these lessons about praying in communion with Mary. Use examples from Scripture, class notes and discussion, and your own life.

Full, Conscious, and Active Participation

Directions: Read the information and respond to the questions.

1. Before you begin, take a minute to write down what you think it means to have full, conscious, and active participation at Mass.

    _____

    _____

    _____

Full Participation

2. How would you define the word "full" in your own words?

    _____

    _____

    _____

3. Write two definitions of the word "full":

    _____

    _____

    _____

4. How do you think that applies to the Mass?

    _____

    _____

    _____

5. Ask yourself the following questions:

> Do I stay attentive during Mass?

> Do I read the readings and reflect on them ahead of time?

> Do I pay attention to the priest's or deacon's homily?

> Do I say the communal prayers?

> Do I sing the hymns?

6. What is one goal you would like to set for yourself so you can participate more fully at Mass?

_____

_____

_____

Conscious Participation

In order to be more conscious during Mass, it helps us to learn the meaning or origin behind what we say and do during the Mass. Most of the responses that we say and things we do come from the Bible. Look up the origins of the following three responses.

7. Lord, I am not worthy that you should enter under my roof, but only say the words and my soul shall be healed.

Read Matthew 8:8 and record what it says.

_____

_____

_____

8. When we eat this Bread and drink this Cup, we proclaim your Death, O Lord, until you come again.

Read 1 Corinthians 11:26 and record what it says.

_____

_____

_____

9. Holy, Holy, Holy, Lord God of Hosts. Heaven and earth are full of your glory, Hosanna in the highest. Blessed is he who comes in the name of the Lord. Hosanna in the highest.

Read Isaiah 6:3 and Matthew 21:9 and record what they say.

_____

_____

_____

_____

_____

_____

Active Participation

10. What is one posture we use at Mass?

_____

What does this posture mean? When do we use it in the Mass?

_____

_____

_____

_____

11. What is another posture we use at Mass?

_____

What does this posture mean? When do we use it in the Mass?

_____

_____

_____

_____

12. What is another posture we use at Mass?

   _____

   What does this posture mean? When do we use it in the Mass?

   _____

   _____

   _____

   _____

   _____

13. Look back at your original answer as to what it means to have full, conscious, and active participation in the Mass. Have your thoughts changed? How?

   _____

   _____

   _____

   _____

   _____

   _____

Pray without Ceasing

Directions: Read the Scripture passage, then answer the question that follows.

1 Thessalonians 5:12-22

We ask you, brothers, to respect those who are laboring among you and who are over you in the Lord and who admonish you, and to show esteem for them with special love on account of their work. Be at peace among yourselves.

We urge you, brothers, admonish the idle, cheer the fainthearted, support the weak, be patient with all.

See that no one returns evil for evil; rather, always seek what is good [both] for each other and for all.

Rejoice always.

Pray without ceasing.

In all circumstances give thanks, for this is the will of God for you in Christ Jesus.

Do not quench the Spirit.

Do not despise prophetic utterances.

Test everything; retain what is good.

Refrain from every kind of evil.

What kind of "routine" does this Scripture advise us to have?

_____

_____

The Liturgy of the Hours

Directions: Read the information, then fill in the blanks as your class discussion proceeds.

The Liturgy of the Hours is intended to become the _____ of the whole People of God. In it Christ himself "continues his priestly work through his Church." His members _____ according to their own place in the Church and the circumstances of their lives: priests devoted to the pastoral _____, because they are called to remain diligent in prayer and the service of the word; religious, by the charism of their consecrated _____; all the faithful as much as possible: "Pastors of souls should see to it that the principal hours, especially _____, are celebrated in common in church on Sundays and on the more solemn feasts. The laity, too, are encouraged to recite the _____ office, either with the priests, or among themselves, or even individually." (CCC _____)

What that means is the whole Church can participate in the Liturgy of the Hours, so at any point during the day, someone around the _____ is praying that prayer of the Church. The pope, cardinals, bishops, priests, nuns, sisters, brothers, and _____ are all obligated to pray the full sequence of the hours, observing as closely as possible the true time of day. When laypeople pray the Liturgy of the Hours, they are _____ the greater Church in doing so. The tradition of praying the Hours came from communities setting aside times for prayer as part of the _____ to call people to be with the Lord and their community. The Liturgy of the Hours is based almost entirely on _____, and is on a four-week cycle. The names and times of the different hours to pray are as follows:

The Various Hours and Their Names

Time of the day	Latin name	English name
During the Night	Matins	Readings
Sunrise (traditionally 6 am)	Lauds	Morning Prayer
First Hour of the Day	Prime	(Now part of Morning prayer)
Third Hour of the Day (traditionally 9 am)	Terce	Midmorning Prayer
Sixth Hour of the Day (traditionally noon)	Sext	Midday Prayer
Ninth Hour of the Day (traditionally 3 pm)	None	Midafternoon Prayer
As evening approaches (traditionally 6 pm)	Vespers	Evening Prayer
Nightfall (traditionally 9 pm)	Compline	Night Prayer

I Look at Him, and He Looks at Me

Directions: Read the essay and then answer the focus and reflection questions.

St. John Vianney was a priest in Ars, France in the 1800s. One day, a peasant entered his small church and sat in the last pew. He stayed for a while and then left. The next day, the peasant returned. He always sat in the last pew, apparently doing nothing.

One day the saint walked over to the peasant and asked him, "My good fellow, what are you doing here? You seem to be doing nothing. Are you praying?"

The peasant pointed to the Blessed Sacrament and said in reply, "I look at Him, and He looks at me."

The peasant's response sums up what contemplative prayer is, and the type of prayer we can experience when we participate in the Adoration of the Blessed Sacrament.

Adoration of the Blessed Sacrament is a way to spend time with Jesus as He is truly present in the consecrated host. The consecrated host is placed in a golden vessel called a monstrance and placed on the altar. When we adore the Blessed Sacrament, we express our love for Jesus, and contemplate (or think deeply about and marvel at) the awesome mystery that Jesus is truly present with us. We can do this in silence, or with readings and hymns.

As part of the Church's official liturgy, Adoration is available in most parishes on the evening of Holy Thursday. Many parishes also offer Adoration on a particular day of the week. Some parishes have perpetual Adoration, which means that Adoration is available 24 hours a day, 7 days a week. In those parishes, people sign up as adorers for certain times each week to make sure someone is with Jesus at all times.

Eucharistic Adoration is a blessing we should all experience. In 1979, Pope St. John Paul II gave a speech in which he discussed Adoration of the Blessed Sacrament. He said, "It is especially in the Eucharist that the power and the love of the Lord are given to us. ...The visit to the Blessed Sacrament is a great treasure of the Catholic faith. It nourishes social love and gives us opportunities for adoration and thanksgiving, for reparation and supplication. ...The Blessed Sacrament is Jesus' Real Presence in the fullest sense: the substantial presence by which the whole and complete Christ, God and man, are present. The Eucharist, in the Mass and outside of the Mass, is the Body and Blood of Jesus Christ, and is therefore deserving of the worship that is given to the living God, and to Him alone."

1. Who was St. John Vianney? _____

2. How did the peasant describe what he was doing in St. John Vianney's church?

   _____

3. What is Eucharistic Adoration? _____

   _____

4. What is a monstrance? _____

5. What does it mean to contemplate something?

   _____

6. Why does Pope St. John Paul II say Eucharistic Adoration is a great treasure?

   _____

   _____

Reflection Question

Have you ever contemplated something? Describe the experience using all five senses: What did you see, hear, taste, touch, and smell?

_____

_____

_____

_____

_____

Devotional Prayer: The Stations of the Cross

Directions: Read about devotional prayer, then complete your assigned station.

There are several forms of prayer, or ways to speak to God in prayer. These include prayer of blessing or adoration, petition, intercession, thanksgiving, and praise. Other expressions of prayer tell us about how we enter into communion with God in prayer. These include contemplative prayer, such as Adoration, meditative prayer, praying with Sacred Scripture, and devotional prayer.

Meditative prayer seeks to focus our minds on God and specifically to discern what He is calling us to do. When we pray with Scripture, we seek to understand and unite our hearts with God: we encounter God Himself in Sacred Scripture.

Devotional prayers come from where the Gospel and our own faith and culture meet. The Liturgy – the official prayer of the Church – is the center of the Church's life and, ideally, where all other forms of prayer should point us. One of the most popular devotional prayers is the Stations of the Cross. In this prayer we focus on the Passion of Jesus. This tradition was begun by pilgrims who traveled to Jerusalem to follow the path of Jesus to the Cross. Although not everyone will be able to travel to the Holy Land, the Stations of the Cross allow us all to follow Jesus' path. The 14 Stations of the Cross are often found in churches as a series of small plaques or icons, or large works of art.

Your Station

Give the Scripture passage or a description of this station

_____

_____

_____

_____

_____

We adore you, O Christ, and we praise You, because by Your holy Cross You have redeemed the world.

Add your own prayer that relates to your station:

_____

_____

_____

_____

_____

Draw a depiction of the station you have been assigned.

The _____ Station

Prayer Chart

	What do you already know about this type of prayer?	What is one question you have about this type of prayer?	What did you learn about this type of prayer today?
Novena Summary of Acts 1:14			
The Rosary Summary of Luke 1:28 and Luke 1:42			

	What do you already know about this type of prayer?	What is one question you have about this type of prayer?	What did you learn about this type of prayer today?
Veneration of Relics Summary of Acts 19:11-12			
Pilgrimage Summary of Hebrews 11:16			

Shout Joyfully to the LORD

Directions: Read Psalm 100 below and make up a melody for it. Do not use a popular song or tune you already know.

Shout joyfully to the LORD, all you lands;

serve the LORD with gladness;

come before him with joyful song.

Know that the LORD is God,

he made us, we belong to him,

we are his people, the flock he shepherds.

Enter his gates with thanksgiving,

his courts with praise.

Give thanks to him, bless his name;

good indeed is the LORD,

His mercy endures forever,

his faithfulness lasts through every generation.

Image above: *David Playing the Harp*, by Jan de Bray.

The Psalms

The book of Psalms is made up of 150 songs, poems, and prayers. Many are hymns, or songs of praise, that were written to be a part of official worship, praising God for His creation and work. Psalms of thanksgiving thank God for saving the sacred author from a dangerous or sorrowful situation. The wisdom psalms focus on increasing one's understanding and following the ways of the Lord. These often show evidence of the historical time in which they were written. In the psalms of lament, the sacred authors lifted their sorrows to God (even as most end on a hopeful note). Most of the psalms are psalms of lament.

In a different category are the royal psalms. These were written to praise the reigning king. Later Christians interpreted these as being about the Savior, Jesus Christ.

We can think of the psalms as "a school of prayer." Not only do they serve as models to follow when we pray, but they also inspire us to express our own intentions and hopes toward God.

Directions: Look up and read the following psalms. Write a summary of the psalm in the left column, and note which type of psalm it is in the right column. Not every psalm will fit into only one category.

		Summary of psalm	Type of psalm (hymn, lament, thanksgiving, royal, or wisdom)
1	Psalm 20		
2	Psalm 90		

	Summary of psalm	Type of psalm (hymn, lament, thanksgiving, royal, or wisdom)
3 Psalm 149		
4 Psalm 37		
5 Psalm 130		
6 Psalm 100		

Lectio Divina

Directions: Read the information with your classmates, then write out the four steps of the *Lectio Divina*.

God Himself is in the Sacred Scriptures. When we read the Bible, we are not simply taking in a piece of information or reading a story. It is an encounter with God Himself! "Indeed, the word of God is living and effective, sharper than any two-edged sword, penetrating even between soul and spirit, joints and marrow, and able to discern reflections and thoughts of the heart" (Hebrews 4:12).

Since God is all knowing, and God is Truth, He knows our hearts even better than we do, and He will communicate to us through His word exactly what we need at any given moment. This is one reason we don't stop reading the Bible when we've read it only once. We read it at every Holy Mass, and throughout our lives!

It is important to remember that we should not read the Bible as we would read a history book or a story. We don't need to – and we shouldn't! – simply analyze the text of the Bible as we might to prepare to write an English paper. We read it to be with God and enter into a dialogue with Him.

One ancient way of entering into this dialogue is called *Lectio Divina* (which means "divine reading," and is pronounced lexio di-veen-ah). Generally speaking, it is a four-step process, but remember that it is not a science! The goal is not to follow specific steps in order, but to enter into that dialogue with God through Scripture. St. Teresa of Ávila called prayer "a conversation between friends." This is what *Lectio Divina* can help you have.

Write the four steps in *Lectio Divina* and what they mean as you discuss them with your teacher.

1. _____

2. _____

3. _____

4. _____

Not Yesterday, nor Tomorrow, but Today

Directions: Read the information and the quote from the *Catechism of the Catholic Church*, then answer the questions that follow.

Our lives often feel busy, and many things seem to change very fast sometimes. Do you ever wonder how God can keep up? Sometimes you might feel too busy to read the Bible or to pray. But ironically, it is during those times that praying is even more important! By praying with Scripture, God offers us all exactly what we need, no matter how fast things change or how busy we are. Through life's ups and downs, and through the ordinary, even boring times, we need only open our hearts to His promptings.

Catechism of the Catholic Church no. 2659

We learn to pray at certain moments by hearing the Word of the Lord and sharing in his Paschal mystery, but his Spirit is offered us at all times, in the events of *each day*, to make prayer spring up from us. Jesus' teaching about praying to our Father is in the same vein as his teaching about providence: time is in the Father's hands; it is in the present that we encounter him, not yesterday nor tomorrow, but today: "O that *today* you would hearken to his voice! Harden not your hearts."

1. Do you tend to spend most of your time thinking about what has happened, what will happen, or what is happening? Why do you think so?

   _____

   _____

2. What can you do *today* to listen to God's voice?

   _____

   _____

   _____

Prayer and Our Old Testament Role Models

Directions: Read the information about each individual, look up and read the Scripture passages, and then write some ways he could be a role model for us in prayer.

Role Model	Scripture passages	How he could be a role model for us
Abraham God promised Abraham, "I will make you into a great nation and I will bless you; I will make your name great, and you will be a blessing." God gives Abraham many commands that Abraham does not understand, and tests Abraham's faith by asking Abraham to sacrifice his son, Isaac. Abraham obeys God because he has faith in His promises.	Genesis 12:4 Genesis 15:2-6 Genesis 18:16-33	
Jacob Jacob was the grandson of Abraham – his father was Abraham's son Isaac. An angel of God renamed him Israel. Jacob is the ancestor of the Twelve Tribes of Israel.	Genesis 32:24-31 Luke 18:1-8	
David King David, a descendant of Abraham, was king of Israel for 40 years. David was a great king but, like all human beings, he was a sinner. God rebuked him for his sins. David is credited with writing almost half the psalms in the book of Psalms.	Psalm 51	

Mary Is a Model of Prayer

Directions: Use the 12 Mary Timeline Cards to answer the questions. The cards come from events in Luke 1, 2, 8, 11, John 19, and Acts 1. You may read those chapters if you need help.

1. After you have put the cards in chronological order, write the letter of each card in order.

    _____

2. Which of the events in Mary's life (including those in the strips and other events you recall from her life) do you think required the greatest faith?

    _____

    _____

3. Which event in Mary's life do you think was most joyful for her? Explain.

    _____

    _____

4. Which event do you think was most sorrowful? Explain.

    _____

    _____

5. Which event do you think was hardest for her to understand? Explain.

    _____

    _____

6. How does Mary respond to all of these events? What can her response teach us?

    _____

    _____

Jesus Teaches Us to Pray

Directions: Look up the Bible verses and write a one- or two-sentence analysis of Jesus' teaching about prayer.

1. Matthew 21:21-22:

_____

_____

_____

2. Luke 11:5-8:

_____

_____

_____

3. Luke 11:11-13:

_____

_____

_____

4. Matthew 6:5-8:

_____

_____

_____

5. Matthew 7:7-11:

_____

_____

_____

_____

_____

_____

6. Mark 11:25:

_____

_____

_____

_____

_____

_____

Jesus in the Garden of Gethsemane,
St. John's Anglican Church, Ashfield,
New South Wales

Prayer and the Saints

Directions: Answer the questions based on the saint you learned about.

1. Which saint did you read about? _____

2. Give a brief summary of his or her life.

_____

_____

_____

3. In which situations did this person pray?

_____

_____

4. How did this person respond to Jesus' teaching on prayer?

_____

_____

_____

5. We can ask those holy ones who have gone before us for their intercession. On the lines below, write a prayer asking this saint to pray for you in a special way.

_____

_____

_____

_____

_____

My Prayer Life

Directions: Think about ways you can apply what you have learned in this unit to your own prayer life in the summer ahead. Try to set goals for prayer that are challenging, but achievable. Explain what you will do and how you hope to grow closer to Christ on the lines below.

_____

_____

_____

_____

_____

_____

_____

_____

_____

_____

_____

_____

_____

_____

_____

_____

_____